CAUSATION IN CONSTRUCTION LAW

Principles and Methods of Analysis

By

Daniel Atkinson

BSc(Hons) LLB(Hons) CEng FICE FCIArb DipIArb FInstCES Barrister (non-practising)

To Gillian

© Daniel Atkinson Limited 2007

British Library Cataloguing
In Publication Data
A catalogue record for this
Book is available from
The British Library

ISBN 978-0-9557293-0-0

Published by
Daniel Atkinson Limited
London

PREFACE

Construction raises complex issues of the rights, obligations and remedies of parties in relation to the progress of the construction project in which they are engaged. The complexity of the issue arises from

a)   the need to interpret the terms of the governing legal relationship between the parties, in order to fix the incidence of liability and to determine the measure of compensation if any,

b)   the multitude of participants and events in a construction project, and

c)   the difficulty of the principles of causation in law.

The Construction Enterprise

There are numerous discrete events that can affect the progress of a construction enterprise.

The overall enterprise is usually divided and scaled down into separate projects and phases and into manageable work packages carried out by subcontractors and suppliers. The division increases the number of participants and increases the possibilities of actions or inactions that affect progress. The possibility of organisational and communication problems between participants is accentuated by the frequent interdependence, both physically and in time, of each operation and process in the overall enterprise. Inevitably, the long overall enterprise period means that there are changes in personnel adding further to the possibilities.

The physical environment in which the construction enterprise is carried out will determine the incidence of events that will affect progress. Not all the events can be predicted or predicted with any accuracy. For instance, the geographic location of each project will determine the incidence of wind, wave, current, temperature or earthquake events. The site itself will comprise pre-existing physical conditions measured for instance by the nature and properties of ground strata, the existence of ground water and susceptibility to flooding, faults, swallow holes, the presence of capped reservoirs of methane and the presence of toxic materials in existing structures.

Other events relate to legal requirements such as import and export of machinery or health and safety or control of pollution or nuisance that may affect progress of each project.

The incidence and extent of liability for events is dependent not only on the nature and timing of the event but also on the allocation of risk between the parties. That may depend not only on express and implied terms of a contract in relation to the event itself, but also on the reactive obligations and on concepts of foreseeability, probability and remoteness in law.

Inevitably, in view of the complexity of construction enterprises each construction case needs to be considered on its own facts. Nonetheless, it is possible to identify legal principles that will apply.

The Principles of Causation in Construction Law

The modern developments in construction law which has affected causation issues have been the better understanding of risks in construction and the development and availability of powerful computers and programmes to analyse complex construction projects.

The question of causation in construction law raises difficult issues sufficiently frequently for it to have created a specialist area inhabited by experts using increasingly sophisticated programme analysis. Such opinion evidence is frequently unhelpful in resolving the issues.

In this Book I have attempted to explain the law of causation as I understand it applies to construction law and to identify the principles that need to be applied. I have set out the practical steps to be taking in the consideration of the incidence of liability.

In doing so, I have drawn from cases not only in construction but also in other areas of law. There is a risk in transposing considerations in one area of law to another, particularly where the decisions are heavily influenced by policy considerations and the need to administer justice. Nonetheless the concepts and general principles of causation and concepts of risk, loss of chance and apportionment developed in such cases provide a better understanding of causation in construction law.

Definition of Terms

I have attempted to use the common meaning of terms wherever possible and in particular as defined in BS 6079-2: 2000 Project Management Vocabulary.

The term "project" is used to define the particular part of the human endeavour such as the design by a firm of consultants, the manufacture of equipment by the manufacturer or the construction of a contractor and is the summation of discrete activities.

The term "activities" is an operation or process which usually will have a duration as well as consuming resources. The term is often used in practice to describe any line item in a programme. In that case the activity may be the individuals making up the design team, or the drawings and calculations, the parts of the equipment to be manufactured instead of the operations to be carried out to complete the construction and in that case may not consume any resource.

The term "events" is used to define an incidence that may have an effect on progress and the term includes the incidence of natural forces as well as human intervention by action or inaction.

The term "construction contract" refers to any binding contract for a project that involves the design and/or construction of buildings or any engineering works intended to be fixed to land.

The phrase "Employer" is used to describe the contracting party engaging the Contractor to carry out the project. Phrases such as "purchaser" or "owner" are also commonly adopted for the same relationship and in subcontracting arrangements the "Employer" under the subcontract will be the "Contractor" under the main contract.

The phrase "Contractor" is used to describe the contracting party engaged to carry out the project.

The Meaning of "Delay"

I have not attempted a definition of the term "delay" although it is used throughout this Book and in many decided cases. The term is understood in common usage to be a comparative measure of the difference in a measure of time between two situations from which the "delay" is inferred. The measure of time may be by date such as a completion date or a start dat, or by a period such as the duration of an activity.

That flexible meaning of the term "delay" is used in this book and its precise meaning is to be taken from the context in which it is used.

Examples and Illustrations

I have used examples to illustrate the operation of the legal principles together with graphic illustration using the linked bar chart presentation.

I have also used a simple project to explain the different methods of analysis. This theoretical project has been designed to illustrate the common difficulties and inherent inaccuracies that need to be considered in any analysis.

Daniel Atkinson September 2007

ABOUT THE AUTHOR

Daniel Atkinson is a chartered civil engineer and for 18 years was involved in projects as diverse as Port Developments, Marine and Offshore Facilities, Roads and Bridges, Tunnels and Buildings. He has worked abroad as well as in the UK. In that time he has used computers and computer programming at each of the developing stages of the technology mostly in design works.

After 18 years of a successful career, he embarked on a different career. In 1987, he was appointed as head of the commercial department of a large engineering consultancy practice before devoting all of his time from 1989 onwards to resolving disputes. In 2000, Daniel Atkinson Limited was established.

He studied law for three years whilst still in full employment and graduated with an LLB (Honours) in 1992. He then proceeded to study for the Bar in order to gain further practical insight into the application of law in resolving disputes and was called to the Bar as a non-practising Barrister in 1994.

He has been involved in the resolution of disputes in all engineering disciplines including not only civil engineering but also mechanical engineering and process engineering and in dispute resolution processes of mediation, adjudication and arbitration.

In all these disputes Daniel Atkinson has adopted a hands-on approach using a developed a focussed approach to analysis and resolution, using his knowledge of computerised data management and diagnostic techniques.

The projects have involved Scots, Danish, Dutch, French, Belarus, Bangladesh, Dutch and Greek Law as well as English Law and have therefore involved an appreciation of international procedures and cultures.

Daniel Atkinson lectures extensively both in the UK and Europe on all the standard forms and on the resolution of disputes, the preparation and defending of claims and generally on commercial awareness. He writes regularly for various magazines and is author of Chapter 4.1 of the Construction Law Handbook published by Thomas Telford.

The website www.atkinson-law.com contains extensive articles on construction law, of which Daniel Atkinson is the sole proprietor.

Daniel Atkinson can be contacted directly by e-mail at daniel@atkinson-law.com

TABLE OF CONTENTS

TABLE OF CASES

CHAPTER 1 - CAUSATION IN LAW

1.1. CAUSATION

Common Concepts of Causation

1.1   The true nature of causation has been considered by philosophers and lawyers for centuries. The problem in law is that the judicial approach must attribute responsibility for damage on the basis of substantial justice in the circumstances and on the merits of the case. It is not sufficient simply to establish causation as a fact.

1.2   Concepts of causation of fact may identify many possible causes of the event that culminated in the damage claimed. There may be events that contribute to the necessary circumstances, some may combine to cause the damage and some may cause the same damage.

1.3   The judicial approach must also consider issues of justice and fairness in the context of the particular obligation and in the case of contracts, the agreed allocation of risk.

1.4   Causation in law is not the application of self-sufficient expressions of logic or judicial instinct, but a condition of liability based on fairness and justice. In *Fairchild v Glenhaven Funeral Services Ltd* [2002] UKHL 22 Lord Hoffmann considered that the rules laying down causal requirements were not autonomous expressions of some form of logic but were part of the conditions of legal liability.

1.5   Judicial decisions on causation are often expressed in terms of "common sense" and/or "dominant or effective cause". These expressions do not identify a method of analysis of causation, but rather are classifications of the decision. The expressions are often used when the decision is based on inference and distinguish sequences of events which ordinary human experience suggests are normal and familiar as opposed to abnormal and extraordinary. Frequently the expressions are used without any disclosed analysis of the events.

1.6   There are three common concepts of causation.

    1.6.1   The "But For" Test;

    1.6.2   New Intervening Event and Risk Allocation;

    1.6.3   The Principled Approach.

1.7   The first concept of the "but-for" test is a concept of causation in fact. The uncertainties of fact and the need for justice mean that any scientific or logical theory may be insufficient to allocate liability. This is particularly the case with the "but - for" test.

1.8   The second concept of the New Intervening Event is limited in application and requires value judgments as to the probability of occurrence of the event in issue and consideration of the legal relationship. In many cases, the concept does not provide a solution. When it does apply, it can provide a means of identifying the sole cause of the damage.

1.9   Only the third concept is a complete method of analysis of legal causation. The Principled Approach is described below by reference to decided cases in different areas of law. Different policy considerations may apply in different areas of law, but the assumption that has been made is that the Principled Approach is sufficiently robust to allow that requirement to be dealt with as part of the approach.

1.10   Each of the three concepts is examined below in the context of construction practices and problems and by reference to examples to demonstrate the differences between each approach.

1.11   As an aid to clarity, the term "initial event" is used below to mean

    1.11.1   a breach of contract or a breach of duty by the Defendant, such as the failure to give access or the failure to provide information as required by the contract, or the failure of a duty to warn; or

    1.11.2   an action of the Defendant which in law entitles the Claimant to a remedy, such as an instructed variation under a contract, or

    1.11.3   the incidence of a risk event the responsibility of the Defendant, such as the occurrence of physical conditions or weather or industrial action or changes in law which under the contract allow the Claimant compensation.

The term "damage" is used to mean any consequences of an initial event including delay or disruption to progress as well as additional costs.

The Limits of Causation in Fact

1.12   Often in construction disputes causation in law is not a significant issue, but is obvious without the need for any detailed factual or legal analysis.

1.13   When the issue of causation does arise as a significant issue, the complex inter-relation of participants and events in the construction enterprise means that analysis is likely to be complex. The usual approach when the issue is delay is a programme analysis which frequently is logically inaccurate. The analysis in some cases can simply obscure the issue of liability.

1.14   Despite the frequent use of programme analysis, there is no general rule of causation to allocate liability for damage. There are concepts and principles that are developed in decided cases that assist in identifying the appropriate approach in a particular situation. The causal requirements may differ between cases in order to provide a just and fair solution.

1.15   In *Fairchild v Glenhaven Funeral Services Ltd* [2002] UKHL 22 Lord Hoffmann
        considered that the causal requirements for liability often varied, sometimes quite
        subtly, from case to case. He observed that since the causal requirements for liability
        were always a matter of law, these variations represented legal differences that were
        driven by the recognition that the just solution to different kinds of case might require
        different causal requirement rules. Although the principle was stated in a case in
        medical negligence, the judicial approach applies equally in construction law.

1.16   Causation in law is based on inference or induction from uniformity of sequence
        between two events based on ordinary everyday life and thoughts and expressions and
        not philosophical speculation, per Lord Wright in *Monarch Steamship Co Ltd v
        Karlshamns Oljefabriker* [1949]HL AC196.

1.17   Logical or scientific theory may be irrelevant to establishing legal liability. In *London
        Underground Limited v Citylink Telecommunications Ltd* [2007] EWHC 1749 (TCC)
        Ramsey J accepted that in a complex project in which the basis for entitlement to
        extension of time was fairness and reasonableness that it may not be best suited to
        analysis by the critical path method. It was accepted that the approach to causation
        was a matter which, if at all, could only be established by drawing inferences as
        appropriate. It was held that the question of what was fair and reasonable was not tied
        to a particular analysis and the assessment necessarily had a subjective element.

1.18   It may be possible to identify a sole cause from a number of events but in some cases,
        there may be more than one event causing the damage. Some events may be discarded
        as a cause in law. There may however be multiple causes of the same damage. In
        Stapley v Gypsum Mines Ltd [1953] HL AC 663 Lord Reid recognised the difficulty of
        the task of allocating liability.

        1.18.1   Lord Reid considered that any valid logical or scientific theory of causation
                  was quite irrelevant. The question had to be determined by applying common
                  sense to the facts of each particular case.

        1.18.2   He observed that as a matter of history several people might have been at fault
                  and that if any one of them had acted properly the accident would not have
                  happened, but that did not mean that the accident must be regarded as having
                  been caused by the faults of all of them.

        1.18.3   He considered that one must discriminate between those faults that must be
                  regarded as being too remote and those that must not. Sometimes it was proper
                  to discard all but one and to regard that one as the sole cause, but in other
                  cases, it was proper to regard two or more as having jointly caused the
                  accident.

        1.18.4   He considered that there was no test that could be applied generally.

1.19   In matters of causation in law, each case has to be judged on its own facts in the
        context of the legal relationship between those involved and the obligation in issue
        Stapley v Gypsum Mines Ltd [1953]HL AC 663.

The Judicial Approach to Causation

1.20   It is difficult to identify from the decided cases in construction any one practical method of analysis to allocate responsibility for damage due to a particular event. There are constant references to the application of common sense, but that does not lead to any practical principle that can be applied. Common sense must mean, by definition, that everyone will have the same point of view of causation on the facts. The cases show that judges will differ in their views on the same facts, each appealing to common sense.

1.21   The modern approach in law is to focus not only on causation in fact but also to ask whether the defendant should be liable for the damage. It is still necessary to establish causation in fact but that is not sufficient. By approaching the issue as a question of law, causation has a more precise meaning. The judicial approach to causation embraces concepts such as the probability of damage, the loss of chance and the allocation of risk. This emphasis on risk allocation is much closer to the approach adopted in the drafting of modern construction contracts.

1.22   In this approach, the appeal to common sense should be a final check on the result of the analysis, to establish whether it is consistent with the judge's sense of justice, which itself must fit the concepts of law from decided cases. It is therefore a principled approach in which public policy may play a role but certainly fairness, with necessary value judgments of both fact and law. Many of the mechanisms that have been developed, frequently with Latin tags, are simply means of identifying the common principles that apply.

1.23   In the principled approach the purpose and scope of the rule of law or obligation is vital in determining causation. In *Empress Car Company (Abertillery) Ltd. v. National Rivers Authority* [1998]HL Lord Hoffman stated that one could not give a common sense answer to a question of causation for the purposes of attributing responsibility without knowing the purpose and scope of the rule.

1.24   In *Rahman v Arearose Ltd* [2001] QB351 Laws LJ explained that although causation was a matter of common sense it also imported the value judgment whether there should be liability for the event.

   1.24.1   Laws LJ considered that in all these cases of causation, the real question was what damage should be the responsibility of the defendant.

   1.24.2   The nature of his duty was relevant as was causation, but it could only be understood in light of the kind of harm which the defendant had a duty to guard the claimant against.

   1.24.3   The various concepts of causation were no more than mechanisms that the law had developed to articulate in practice the extent of any liable defendant's responsibility for the loss and damage that the claimant has suffered.

1.25   The causal requirement rules are intended to produce a just result by delimiting the scope of liability by reference to the purpose of the rule of law as stated by Lord Hoffmann in *Fairchild v Glenhaven Funeral Services Ltd* [2002] UKHL 22. He stated the general principle that causal requirements have to be adapted to allocate liability where it is just and reasonable to do so whether in tort, contract or statute. The causal requirements are always adapted to conform to the grounds upon which liability is imposed.

1.26   In construction contracts, this principled approach requires consideration of the nature of the contract and the agreed allocation of risk. The issue is the extent of liability intended by the parties to the contract to be imposed for damage for a particular event and is formulated in terms of legal liability instead of solely a factual enquiry. In short, it requires the right legal question to be asked.

1.2. JUDICIAL COMMON SENSE

1.27   Reference is usually made to common sense when the requirements of justice lead to a different allocation of liability than the application of general factual principles of causation.

1.28   The reference to commonsense usually means a restriction of the consequences of the application of factual rules or principles of causation *Galoo Ltd v Bright Grahame Murray* [1993]CA 1 WLR 1360.

1.29   A pragmatic approach is required and not simply the application of logical principles of causation. In *John Holland Construction & Engineering Pty Ltd v Kvaerner RJ Brown Pty Ltd*, [1996] 82BLR83 the Supreme Court of Victoria formulated the approach by stating that causation for the purposes of a claim for damages must be determined by the application of common sense to the logical principles of causation.

1.30   Factual analysis particularly based on the "but-for" test does not provide a full answer and in some cases is best avoided. It may be sufficient to establish liability in some situations that the event is "a" cause and not "the" cause of the damage *Thomas Chapman v Tangmere Airfield Nurseries Limited* [1998]CA .

1.31   Where a number of factors combine a more sophisticated approach than the "but for" is required. It is necessary to apply common sense with regard to the purpose for which the selection of the cause is being made *Casey v Morane Ltd* [2000] CA Lord Justice Mance. The link between the application of common sense and the obligation or duty being considered is the important aspect of the principled approach. The exercise is one of judgment and selection, bearing in mind the nature of the issue, the context in which and the purpose for which the selection of a cause is being made.

1.32   The appeal to "common sense" should not prevent a proper explanation of the decision and the reason for the adoption of a causal relationship in one situation and not another *Fairchild v Glenhaven Funeral Services Ltd* [2002] UKHL 22 Lord Hoffmann.

1.33   Causation is a matter of inference and in construction is based on expert reports, but over-elaborate analysis should be avoided *John Doyle Construction Limited v Laing Management (Scotland) Limited* [2004] 1BLR 295 Inner House the Inner House.

1.34   It appears then that English law does not easily accept the results of scientific analysis. The concern is justified in relation to programme analysis in construction.   The analyses are frequently flawed and there can be little confidence in the methods adopted. The facts are many, varied, and disputed. The experts usually admit that the different methods will give different results. In some cases, the experts adopt incorrect logic and ignore the evidence.

1.35   It is not surprising that reference is frequently made to the everyday understanding of causation, which is referred to as "common sense".

1.36   The problem with the concept of common sense is that without further definition it is a test that is not easy to apply to practical problems that occur in construction.

1.3. DOMINANT OR EFFECTIVE CAUSE

1.37   The terms *"effective cause"*, *"proximate cause"* or *"dominant cause"* are often used to classify the operative cause of damage. The classification is used to distinguish one event as the cause of the damage, from a number of other events that are simply part of the circumstances in which the damage occurred. The classification also distinguishes situations where there is a break in the causal connection making the initial event simply part of the circumstances in which the damage occurred[1].

1.38   Although often used interchangeably, the terms do not have the same meaning. An "effective cause" does not necessarily exclude other events being "effective" or being a "material cause". The term "dominant cause" is intended to classify the event as ruling or prevailing over other events.

1.39   In some circumstances, there may well be no "dominant cause" and more than one cause of equal efficacy. The use of the classification in English Law does not mean that liability is precluded if there is more than one cause of equal efficacy. It is not necessary that one cause should be "dominant". Liability in contract will depend upon the terms of the contract and the intention of the parties.

1.40   When the classification is used, there is no guidance on how the "dominant cause" is to be ascertained. It does not provide a method of legal analysis.

1.41   In *Leyland Shipping Company Ltd v Norwich Union Fire Insurance Society Ltd,* [1918]HL AC 350 a ship was torpedoed by a German submarine and taken into the harbour of le Havre. When a gale sprang up, she was moved to a berth inside the outer breakwater, where she took the ground at each ebb tide. Ultimately, her bulkheads gave way and she sank. She was insured against perils of the sea, but excluding the

---

[1]   The dominant cause approach may in some cases use the concept of new intervening act to establish whether or not the initial event is still effective.

consequences of hostilities. It was held that the *"proximate cause"* of the loss was the damage inflicted by the torpedo, which fell within the exclusion.

1.41.1   The principle is that although the subsequent event played a part, the identification of the hostile act as the "proximate cause" means that it is treated in law as the operative cause of the loss.

1.41.2   The overriding principle in contract is to look at the contract as a whole and to ascertain what the parties had in mind when they identified the particular cause. The "effective cause" is not necessarily the cause that is most proximate in time.

1.41.3   Lord Shaw of Dunfermline observed that causes were often referred to as if they were as distinct from one another as beads in a row or links in a chain. Although the term "chain of causation" was a handy expression it was inadequate since causation was not a chain but a net. He considered that the cause which was truly proximate was that which was proximate in efficiency[2].

1.42   There is little guidance on the identification of the "dominant cause", except for the application of commonsense as understood by the ordinary man taking a broad view *Yorkshire Dale Steamship Co v Minister of War Transport (The Coxwold)* [1942] AC 691.

1.42.1   Lord Wright considered that the choice of the real or efficient cause from out of the whole complex of the facts had to be made by applying commonsense standards.

1.42.2   Causation was as understood by the man in the street, and not as understood by the scientist or the metaphysician.

1.42.3   Cause in the case before him was what a business or seafaring man would take to be the cause without too microscopic analysis but on a broad view.

1.43   In *Monarch Steamship Co Ltd v Karlshamns Oljefabriker* [1949]HL AC196 the ship boilers were defective and delayed leaving Port Said, at the north end of the Suez Canal, until 24 September 1939. By that date, the Second World War had broken out and the British Admiralty prohibited the ship from proceeding to Sweden as intended and ordered her to proceed to, and discharge at, Glasgow. The cargo was eventually trans-shipped in neutral ships and delivered to Sweden at extra cost.

1.43.1   Lord Wright adopted the classification of "dominant cause" and chose unseaworthiness as the cause of the loss.

1.43.2   He considered that unseaworthiness caused the Admiralty order diverting the vessel.

---

[2]   The facts of the case can be analysed using the principles of new intervening act. It could be said that the moving of the ship to a safe harbour was the natural consequence of being torpedoed and not sunk immediately. The break up followed naturally from the incidence of normal weather.

1.43.3   Unseaworthiness was to be picked from the whole complex of circumstances as the dominant cause.

1.43.4   It appears that the important fact in this case was that the outbreak of war was a real possibility in the context of the international situation, and the risk of the embargo increased with each passing day.   The possibility of war was a consideration when the charterparty was made and a war clause was inserted. The delay due to unseaworthiness increased the risk of the embargo that actually occurred[3].

1.44   Where there are two operative causes of equal efficacy in contract, in the sense that if either had ceased the damage would have ceased, that is sufficient to establish liability for damages *Heskell v Continental Express Ltd* [1950]1AllER1033.

1.44.1   Devlin J. considered that common sense was a blunt instrument not suited for probing into minute points.

1.44.2   If the ordinary man thinks that two causes are of approximately equal efficacy, then there should be no interrogation on fine distinctions.

1.45   Usually when it is stated that a breach of contract must first be held to have been an "*effective*" or "*dominant*" cause of loss to give an entitlement to damages, the classification is used in order to distinguish the cause of the loss from merely the occasion for the loss as in *Galoo Limited v Bright Grahame Murray* [1993]CA 1 WLR 1360 and *Phee Farrar Jones Limited v Connaught Mason Limited* [2003] (TCC).   In the latter, HH Judge Toulmin emphasised that if there was an intervening cause which broke the thread of causation, the damage was not the result of the wrongful act of the other party.

1.46   In the situation where the breach of contract was capable on its own of causing the loss and the other causes concurred in the loss, then the party in breach is liable as long as his breach was an effective cause of the loss suffered.   There is no need to choose which cause was the most effective *County Ltd v Girozentrale Securities* [1996] CA.

1.46.1   Beldam LJ observed that the judge at first instance had used the expression "*causa sine qua non*" in the sense not just of a necessary step in the sequence of events leading to the loss but of an event which with others combined to cause the loss.

1.46.2   He considered that otherwise there was no basis for comparing the potency of each event in causing the loss.

---

[3]   If the facts of the case are analysed using the concept of new intervening event, the same result can only be achieved if the incidence of war is not categorised as a new intervening event.   That is difficult to accept unless it is recognised that the parties themselves had considered the increasing possibility of outbreak of war and had inserted the war clause.   On those facts the incidence of war was a risk anticipated by the parties and the delay naturally increased the risk.   The outbreak of war on those facts was not an intervening event, but an event which the parties had put their mind to when the entered into the contract.

1.46.3   Beldam LJ considered that the judge's approach of discarding one of the causes because he regarded it as less effective in causing the result than the others meant that he could have rejected an effective cause merely because he considered another cause had had a greater effect.

1.46.4   Beldam LJ held that such an approach was incorrect.

1.46.5   The risks identified by the parties to the contract might assist in classifying intervening events, but the fact that an event was unforeseen did not mean that the breach of contract did not continue to operate and give rise to liability for the damage.

1.46.6   The fact that the parties contemplated circumstances in which loss could occur might be an indication that such circumstances commonly follow breach of a contract of that kind. This could be helpful in deciding as a fact whether the loss was caused by the breach or merely followed it.

1.46.7   The fact that the parties do not contemplate other circumstances which contributed to the loss and therefore suggesting that such circumstances might not be probable, could not determine the question whether the loss was a consequence of the breach.

1.46.8   The fact that unforeseeable events combine with the breach to cause loss could not alone be a sufficient reason for a decision that the unforeseeable events had superseded the breach of contract as the cause of the loss.

1.46.9   The effects of the breach of contract may continue even though other causes combined to produce the final result.

1.47   In a claim for loss and expense for delay and disruption under a contract, if the loss arises from concurrent causes and a "dominant cause" can be identified then that will be the operative cause *John Doyle Construction Limited v Laing Management (Scotland) Limited* [2004] 1BLR 295 Inner House.

1.47.1   It was held that if an item of loss results from concurrent causes, and one of those causes can be identified as the proximate or dominant cause of the loss, it will be treated as the operative cause, and the person responsible for it will be responsible for the loss.

1.47.2   There may still be liability where there is no dominant cause, for instance delay would have occurred if either event had occurred without the other. The classification adopted in that case is not "dominant cause" but "material cause", again to distinguish the event from others that are simply part of the circumstances.

1.47.3   Where the damage flowing from the delay is financial as opposed to extension of time for completion, and the event that is the employer's responsibility in law is a material cause of the loss, then it may be possible to apportion the loss between the events.

1.48   In *Great Eastern Hotel Company Ltd v John Laing Construction Ltd* [2005] EWHC 181 (TCC) the contractual arrangement was not a simple construction contract where the contractor carries out all the work, with part being carried out by his domestic subcontractors. Instead, it was a construction management agreement and the issue was whether Laing as construction manager could have any liability for delays to the work.

    1.48.1   Great Eastern contracted directly with the trade contractors and Laing simply received its agreed fee for managing the construction. Laing's primary obligation under the agreement was to exercise all reasonable skill, care and diligence of a properly qualified and competent construction manager including managing, administering, planning and coordinating the work with the trade contractors.

    1.48.2   Delays were caused by both Laing and the trade contractors.

    1.48.3   HH Judge Wilcox held that the appropriate test for causation was that if Great Eastern proved that Laing was in breach and the proven breach materially contributed to the loss, then it could recover the whole loss, even if there was another effective contributory cause, provided that there was no double recovery.

    1.48.4   The terms of the contract were relevant in terms of potency and apportionment, but otherwise it was only necessary to show a "material contribution" to the loss to establish liability.

    1.48.5   In applying the test to the claims made by Trade Contractors and settled by Eastern and claimed from Laing, Wilcox J considered that the evidence showed that the "*dominant cause*" of the Trade Contractor delay was in fact delay caused by Laing's proven breaches, thus applying the dominant cause test.

1.49   The judgment of His Honour Judge Fox-Andrews QC in the construction case of *H Fairweather & Co Ltd v London Borough of Wandsworth* [1987]39BLR106 (QBD) recognised that different principles of law may apply to causation in relation to separate legal rights and liabilities and that the "dominant cause" approach in relation to one right may not always be appropriate to determine another separate right. That is an important part of the principled approach to causation.

    1.49.1   HH Judge Fox-Andrews considered the JCT Local Authorities Edition with Quantities 1963 Edition (July 1973 Revision) and the award of an arbitrator for extension of time. Logically the same set of facts might fall within two separate paragraphs of the extension of time clause 23, with one listed event giving the contractor the right to loss and expense under clause 24 and the other not.

    1.49.2   The arbitrator decided that where delay to completion of the works could be allocated to more than one of the events listed in clause 23, the extension had to be granted in respect of the dominant cause, since there was no mechanism for allocating extension between different heads. He decided that the dominant cause of the delays were strikes and made clear in his award that the extension did not entitle the contractor to direct loss or expense.

1.49 3   HH Judge Fox-Andrews held that an extension of time under clause 23(f) was not a condition precedent to recovery of direct loss and expense under clause 24(1)(a). He recognised that the practical effect ordinarily will be that if the architect has refused an extension under clause 23(f) the contractor is unlikely to be successful with the architect on an application under condition 24(1)(a).

1.49.4   HH Judge Fox-Andrews concluded that by using the "dominant cause" test the arbitrator might have decided on an erroneous basis and remitted the matter to the arbitrator for further consideration.

1.49.5   It is clear from the judgment that Judge Fox-Andrews considered that where there were competing causes for delay the contractor may still be entitled to some loss and expense for events listed under Clause 24 even if the dominant cause of delay for the purpose of extension of time might be an event not listed in Clause 24. Adopting the "dominant cause" test for time under Clause 23 when considering entitlement under Clause 24, might unfairly deprive the contractor of loss and expense caused by one of the competing events listed under Clause 24.

CHAPTER 2 – CONCEPTS OF CAUSATION

2.1. THE "BUT FOR" CONCEPT

The Use and Limits of the Concept

2.1   The "but for" concept is frequently used as part of an argument to establish causal connections between actions and events in construction. The concept is central to the method of programme analysis known as the "collapse method".

2.2   The "but-for" concept is a test for causation in fact, but is not sufficiently refined to establish causation in law since it is not capable of distinguishing between the legal potency of events.

2.3   The "but-for" concept is useful in filtering out those events which had no effect on the damage claimed, although even then of limited use. It is not sufficient by itself to establish causation as a fact or in law, something more is required.

2.4   Apart from difficulties of logical analysis, the "but-for" concept gives rise to difficulties in the administration of justice in the allocation of liability due to principles such as the burden of proof and the rule of joint and several liability. It is necessary to check the consequences against common sense and the scope and purpose of the allocation of liability in the particular circumstances.

2.5   A distinction may need to be made for the kind of damage considered, whether time, the levy of liquidated damages or compensation for additional costs.

The "But-For" Test

2.6   The general legal principle is that it is necessary for the "but-for" test of causation to be satisfied, but it is not sufficient without more to establish liability for the damage. This general principle cannot be applied in all cases, since the "but for" test does not always establish causation even as a matter of fact or logic.

2.7   The test may be expressed in two different ways.

2.7.1   The first expression of the "but-for" test is that if the removal of an event from the circumstances leads to the conclusion that the damage would still have occurred, then it can be said that the event is not the cause of the damage. This is a negative assertion of causation.

2.7.2   The second expression of the "but-for" test is that if it can be concluded that the damage would not have occurred if the event had not taken place, then the event can be said to be the cause of the damage. This is a positive assertion of causation.

2.8   In the case of concurrent events in which both independently cause the same damage, such as delay, the first and negative assertion of the "but-for" test leads to a conclusion that neither of two events caused the damage contrary to common sense. The test does not deal adequately with issues of concurrency and indivisible damage.

2.9   The second and positive assertion of the test identifies without distinction all the events that are the necessary condition for the damage. It fails to differentiate between events that create only the circumstances in which other events take place but which are not causes in law. The test does not distinguish between events that are simply coincidence and instead gives each event the same potency. The test does not provide a mechanism for distinguishing conditions from causes. Two examples demonstrate this.

2.9.1   A traveller's luggage is misdelivered[4]. The effect is that the traveller is delayed. The effect of the delay is that the traveller must postpone his journey and instead of embarking on an earlier ship as planned, he embarks on the doomed SS Titanic. The "but-for" test identifies the luggage misdelivery as a cause of the loss. If the traveller had not been delayed he would not have embarked on the Titanic. Yet ordinary everyday experience would suggest that the event was an unfortunate coincidence and simply part of the circumstances.

2.9.2   A taxi-driver drives too fast[5]. The accelerated journey means that the taxi arrives at a point in the journey earlier than if the taxi-driver had observed the speed restrictions. At that point in space and time a tree falls and injures the passenger. Again the "but-for" test identifies the taxi-driver's actions as a cause of the damage whereas commonsense suggests it is sheer coincidence.

Judicial Consideration of the "But-For" Concept

2.10   A number of events may be indispensable and essential actions, conditions, or ingredients for the damage to occur ("*sine qua non*" or "but-for"), but one event may be treated as the real, substantial, direct or effective cause. Other events are then simply part of the circumstances and not a cause in law *Stapley v Gypsum Mines Ltd* [1953]HL AC 663.

2.10.1   Lord Asquith observed that there was a divergence between the philosophic doctrine of causation and the judicial doctrine of responsibility for the consequences of a negligent act.

2.10.2   To a philosopher if an event could not occur unless each of two previous events had preceded it, it could not be said that any event was more responsible for the consequences than another was.

2.10.3   In law however two causes might both be necessary pre-conditions of a particular result, yet if the facts justified the conclusion the one may be treated as the real, substantial, direct or effective cause, and the other dismissed as at best a *cause sine qua non* and ignored for purposes of legal liability.

---

[4]   The example is taken from Lord Bingham in *Chester v Asfar* [2004] UKHL41.

[5]   The example is taken from Lord Walker in *Chester v Asfar* [2004] UKHL41.

2.11   There is a logical fallacy in the assumption that if one event happens after another, then the first must be the cause of the second ("*post hoc ergo propter hoc*") *Quinn v Burch Bros Builders Ltd* [1966]CA 2 QB 370.

      2.11.1   In breach of the subcontract, Burch failed to provide Quinn the plastering subcontractor with a stepladder. There was no obligation on Quinn to do the work without suitable equipment. Quinn voluntarily and without Burch's knowledge chose to use a folded trestle, which he propped against the wall and used as if it were a ladder to allow him to reach the ceiling. He used the trestle without someone footing it to prevent it slipping. While he was standing on the trestle, the foot of it slipped and he fell and broke his heel. He claimed damages.

      2.11.2   It was held that the breach of contract merely gave the Plaintiff the opportunity to injure himself and was the occasion of the injury. It was impossible to say that in reality Quinn's injury was caused in law by the breach of contract.

      2.11.3   Salmon LJ observed that there was always a temptation to fall into the fallacy of *post hoc ergo propter hoc*.

      2.11.4   It was held that it was no less a fallacy even if what happened afterwards could have been foreseen before it occurred.

2.12   In a broad sense, a loss may be the result of a breach of contract, but not everything that is a result in the broad sense is accepted as a result for this purpose in law. Something more is required and it is necessary to look more closely at the breach. The fact that the breach has initiated one train of events rather than another may not be sufficient in itself to establish that there is a causal relationship between the breach and the loss *Alexander v Cambridge Credit Corporation* [1987] 9 NSWLR 310 Court of Appeal of New South Wales[6].

      2.12.1   Mahoney JA illustrated the principle by an example. A defendant promised to give the plaintiff directions at a crossroads, and directed to the left road rather than the right road. In a sense, what happened to the plaintiff on the left road was the result of what the defendant had done. If the plaintiff slipped on that road, or if it collapsed under the plaintiff, or if a car driving down that road and not down the right road struck the plaintiff, the loss was, in a sense, the result of the fact that the plaintiff had been directed to the left road and not the right road.

      2.12.2   However not everything which was a result in the broad sense was accepted as a result for this purpose in the law. The fact alone that it was the defendant's direction, in breach of contract, which put the plaintiff on the left road, without more, would not make the defendant liable for the injury or damage.

      2.12.3   If there was added to the breach the fact that, for example, the left road was known to be dangerous then in that case, the plaintiff might be liable.

---

[6]   Held to represent English Law in *Galoo Ltd v Bright Grahame Murray* [1993]CA 1 WLR 1360.

2.12.4   In relation to losses of that kind, the fact that the breach had initiated one train of events rather than another might not be sufficient in itself. It was necessary to determine whether there was a causal relationship, to look more closely at the breach and what flowed from it.

2.12.5   The facts of the case were that in 1971 the auditors of the Cambridge Credit Corporation, in their annual audit certificates, failed to note that the balance sheet and other accounts did not show provisions which should have been made. If the appropriate note had been made it was highly probable that a Receiver would have been appointed. The company eventually was put into receivership in 1974. The company claimed damages for negligent breach of contract against the auditors for the increased loss it had suffered over the period 1971 and 1974.

2.12.6   The majority of the Court of Appeal held that there was no causal connection between the breach of contract and the loss. All the Judges considered that the "but for" test was not enough, and two of them expressly relied on the application of commonsense.

2.12.7   It was recognized that in a sense the loss resulted from the breach because it allowed the company to continue its business. It would otherwise have gone in a different direction had it not been for the breach. That was not enough, something more was required. It was held that the existence of a company could not be a cause of its trading losses or profits. There had been no detailed examination of the particular things which caused the fall in net value of the company and that was fatal to the case.

2.12.8   The company's case has been that the loss it claims was caused by the breach because, and because alone, the breach allowed the company to continue in existence.

2.12.9   Some of the incidents flowing from its existence might be the results of the breach and some, for example, those flowing from earthquakes or the like, would not be. However, the basis of the plaintiffs' claim has been such that no inquiry had been pursued into what in fact happened and the relationship of what happened to the breach.

2.12.10 That was not enough to establish a causal relationship.

2.13   In tort, the "but for" test is not a definitive test of causation and value judgment has a part to play in resolving causation as an issue of fact. It is all ultimately a matter of common sense. Causation is not susceptible of reduction to a satisfactory formula *March v Stramare* [1991] 171 CLR 506 High Court of Australia.

2.13.1   Sir Anthony Mason CJ [7] observed that commentators subdivided the issue of causation in a given case into two questions.

---

[7]   Held to represent English Law in *Galoo Ltd v Bright Grahame Murray* [1993]CA 1 WLR 1360.

2.13.2   The first question was one of causation in fact to be determined by the application of the "but for" test.

2.13.3   The second question was whether a defendant was in law responsible for damage that his or her negligence had played some part in producing.

2.13.4   He observed that it was said that in determining this second question, considerations of policy have a prominent part to play, as did accepted value judgments.

2.13.5   He held that this approach to the issue of causation placed too much weight on the "but for" test to the exclusion of the "common sense" approach. In addition, the approach seemed wrongly to imply that value judgment should have no part to play in resolving causation as an issue of fact.

2.14   In *BHP Billiton Petroleum Ltd v Dalmine SpA* [2003] EWCA Civ 170 it was argued that the "but for" test asks whether the damage of which the claimant complains would have occurred "but for" the wrongdoing. It was argued that this meant that the claimant had to adduce evidence to show that it is more likely than not, more than fifty per cent probable, that "but for" the defendant's wrongdoing the relevant damage would not have occurred.

2.14.1   The Court of Appeal held that this was an unrealistically theoretical approach.

2.14.2   The role of the "but for" test should not be exaggerated. Its purpose was to eliminate irrelevant causes.

2.14.3   The "but for" test was not of universal application.

2.15   In the medical negligence case of *Chester v Ashfar* [2004] UKHL41 in relation to a doctor's negligent failure to warn a patient of a small but unavoidable risk of surgery, the application of the "but-for" test was examined.

2.15.1   Lord Bingham recognised that in tort the "but for" test did not provide a comprehensive or exclusive test of causation in law. Sometimes, if rarely, it was too restrictive but more often it gave too expansive an answer. In the ordinary run of cases satisfying the "but for" test was necessary but not sufficient.

2.15.2   Lord Walker recognised that the "but for" test needed to be distinguished from situations in which the particular event was simply a coincidence and that it was necessary to examine the scope of the duty and the kind of damage involved.

2.16   In the personal injury case of *Eileen Corr v IBC Vehicles* [2006] EWCACiv331 it was emphasised that the "but-for" test was only the first step by excluding irrelevant causes and was not determinative of liability.

2.16.1   The fact that the defendant's conduct was found to be a cause when applying the "but for" test was not conclusive as to whether he should be held responsible in law.

2.16.2   The function of the casual enquiry in law was to determine which causes were effective for the purpose of attributing legal responsibility. That was the reason for the defendant's breach to have made a material contribution even if it was not the sole, or even the main cause of the claimant's damage.

Application of the "But-For" Test to Construction Problems

2.17   The application of the "but for" test to construction problems is demonstrated below by three examples from decided cases.   The three examples are also used to demonstrate the application of the two concepts of New Intervening Event and the Principled Approach in the next Chapters to show that a different answer to causation may result.

Example 1: Concurrent Events – Shortage of Labour & Inclement Weather

2.18   The central facts are that work is available to be carried out but that no work is carried out on the site for one week and during that period, the contractor does not provide labour on site because of a shortage of labour[8].   The effect of no work during that week is that the contractor is likely to complete the works one week later than the date for completion stated in the contract. In this single event situation, the second expression of the "but for" test leads to the conclusion that the shortage of labour caused one week delay. If there was no shortage of labour then the contractor would not have been delayed, so the shortage is the cause of the delay.

2.19   If a concurrent event is introduced, then the limits of the first part of the "but for" test become apparent.

2.20   During the same week, there is exceptionally adverse inclement weather that would have prevented the contractor carrying out any work even if he had labour.   In that situation the "but for" test leads to the conclusion that neither event causes delay. The removal of either event from the circumstances leads to the conclusion that the damage would still have occurred.

2.20.1   If the shortage of labour is removed from the circumstances the delay would still have occurred, since the adverse inclement weather prevents any work being carried out in that week.   The shortage of labour is not therefore the caused of the delay using the "but-for" test.

2.20.2   Similarly, if instead the exceptionally inclement weather is removed from the circumstances the delay would still have occurred, since the shortage of labour prevents any work being carried out that week.   The exceptional inclement weather is also not the cause of delay using the "but-for" test.

---

[8]   The first simple example was used by Dyson J in *Henry Boot Construction (UK) Limited v Malmaison Hotel (Manchester) Ltd* [1999]70ConLR32.

2.21   If the effect of each event was sequential, then the damage could be divided between each event. The difficulty is the indivisibility of the damage, which in the example is the additional one week required to complete. Both events independently have caused the same damage, the extra week to complete.

2.22   In the example, both the Contractor and the Employer may have competing claims for damages. The general rule is that the burden of proof lies with the Claimant. If the responsibility for both events lies with the Defendant, then the indivisibility of damage does not prevent the Claimant proving that the Defendant caused the damage, in the example an extra week to complete. This logic is the basis of the total or global claim.

2.23   If one event entitles the Claimant to compensation for the damage and the other does not, then the indivisibility of damage causes the Claimant difficulty in proving causation using only the "but-for" test. The test provides no mechanism for consideration of the purpose and intention of the entitlement to compensation, the rule of law in issue. The "but for" test is inadequate as a test for establishing causation in the case of indivisible damage, something more is required.

Example 2: Event During Culpable Delay

2.24   The central facts are that the contractor fails to progress the work as planned. The contractor is responsible for the failure. During the prolonged period arising from his failure, a period of culpable delay, an event occurs which further interrupts progress of the works[9]. Three different scenarios are examined.

2.25   Example 2.1. The contractor's failure affects the critical path and leads to a prolonged period after the planned completion date. The period of culpable delay is after planned completion. The event is a storm, which floods the site. The storm and therefore the flooding would have been avoided altogether if the contractor had not overrun the completion date.

    2.25.1   The "but for" test leads to the conclusion that the event causing the culpable delay caused the damage. The storm would not have had a further effect on progress if the contractor had completed by the contract completion date.

2.26   Example 2.2. Suppose in the second scenario that the prolonged period is within the contract period. The contractor has been delayed on planned programme on part of the works for matters for which he is responsible. That part is not on the critical path to completion so that the contractor is still on course to complete by the contract completion date. The storm occurs during the contract period. If the part had not been delayed, it would have reached a stage of construction that would have prevented the flooding of the site by the storm. The delay caused by the flooding is greater than the "float" on that part and changes the critical path resulting in delay to completion.

---

[9]   The second example (slightly modified) was used by Colman J in *Balfour Beatty Building Ltd v Chestermount Properties Ltd* [1993]62BLR1 QBD.

2.26.1 The "but for" test leads again to the conclusion that the event causing the delay to the part of the works caused the damage; the storm would not have had an effect on progress if the contractor had completed the part by the planned completion date.

2.26.2 The "but-for" test does not provides any mechanism

2.26.2.1 to consider the allocation of risk under the contract during the contract period,

2.26.2.2 to consider whether the contractor was under an obligation to follow the planned programme,

2.26.2.3 to consider whether it was necessary in mitigation of other events for the contractor to allocate his resources differently than planned or

2.26.2.4 to consider the nature of the entitlement sought by the contractor.

2.27   Example 2.3. Suppose again that the event occurred during the period after the completion date, a period of culpable delay. Suppose that the event is not a storm but an instructed variation or statutory or utility interruption under the contract.

2.27.1 Unlike the storm, the variation/interruption cannot be assumed to be time dependant so that it cannot be inferred that the period of culpable delay is directly linked causally to the incidence of the event.

2.27.2 In this example the "but for" test is not sufficient but a secondary or sub-network analysis is required, to establish whether the culpable delay dictated the timing of the instructed variation or interruption, or whether the event was an entirely separate independent event. For instance, the timing of the event may be dictated by the progress of the works or the variation may be necessary only because of the circumstances created by the culpable delay or to the contrary the timing may be determined by factors unconnected with progress or culpable delay.

2.27.3 If the variation/interruption is dependant on the stage of progress of the works, then the "but for" test leads to the conclusion that the additional delay would have occurred even without the period of culpable delay and therefore not caused by the event causing the culpable delay.

2.27.4 If the variation/interruption is necessary only because of the circumstances created by the culpable delay, then the "but for" test leads to the conclusion that the additional delay was caused by the event causing the culpable delay.

2.27.5 If to the contrary, the variation/interruption is independent of the culpable delay then it follows that the event would have occurred without the culpable delay, after the required completion date. The "but-for" test leads to the conclusion that the event causing the culpable delay did not cause the additional delay, but due to concurrency as described in Example 1 neither event caused the concurrent period of culpable delay.

Example 3: Event During Extended Period of Contract

2.28   The central facts are that work on the tunnelling contract is proceeding to completion on course by 31 July. In April, the Architect instructs a variation in accordance with the contract that will add 3 months to the contract period to 31 October. The Architect extends the period for completion to 31 October[10]. The second expression of the "but for" test leads to the conclusion that the variation caused the delay. A fortnight before 31 October when the works as varied were on course for completion, a strike occurs which continues until 31 March the following year. The contractor starts work on 1 April in the following year, but the extent of the shutdown of the site means that instead of taking the planned fortnight to complete, the contractor takes a further six weeks. The extra time is due to maintenance of equipment, which could not be done for seasonal reasons between 1 November and 31 March.

2.28.1   The "but for" test leads to the conclusion that the instructed variation caused all the consequences in both time and cost including the consequences of the seasonal effects on maintenance. The damage would not have occurred if the instruction had not been issued; the contractor would not have been exposed to the risk of strikes and would not have been exposed to seasonal effects preventing the maintenance of the equipment.

2.28.2   The "but-for" test takes no account of the allocation of risk in the particular contract and the expressions of entitlement for variations and delay and is solely a limited analysis of causation in fact.

2.2. THE CONCEPT OF INTERVENING EVENT AND RISK ALLOCATION

The Use and Limits of the Concept

2.29   The concept of New Intervening Event (or the Latin maxim "*novus actus interveniens*") is used to identify one event from many as the cause of damage. The concept only applies when there is a new independent event that is so potent in law that it reduces all other events to background.

2.30   The concept therefore differs from the "but-for" test, since that test is not sufficiently refined to distinguish between the legal potency of events.

2.31   A new intervening event may have different levels of potency.

2.31.1   The new event either prevents the initial event from acting at all or renders its effect legally insignificant.

2.31.2   The initial event continues to act concurrently with the new event, each causing damage.

---

[10]   The third example was used by HH Judge Fox-Andrews QC in *H Fairweather & Co Ltd v London Borough of Wandsworth* [1987]39BLR106 (QBD).

2.31.3   The initial event and the new event are independent of each other and combine to cause damage. Neither event would have caused damage without the other.

2.32   The concept of New Intervening Event eliminates those initial events that are coincidental and simply create the circumstances for the new event to operate and identifies the event that is the real, substantial, direct or effective cause of the damage. The concept only applies in the first situation above. It does not assist when two events operate independently to cause the same indivisible damage. It does not apply in the situation of true concurrency although it may assist in identifying that situation.

2.33   The concept of New Intervening Event focuses on the nature of the chain of events, the legal relationship of the Parties, the allocation of risk and the independence of the new event.

2.34   The concept has been applied to acts by the injured party, to acts of third parties and to natural forces.   In all these situations, the test appears to be the same, based on improbability of occurrence measured in the context of the legal relationship of the claimant and defendant.   The incidence of events *"out of the ordinary course of things"* and events of *"unnatural, extraordinary or unusual character"* are based on the premise that the events have little probability of occurring in particular circumstances. Foreseeability is part of the test of probability but it is only one measure and not the true criterion for causation.

2.35   Whether or not an event is a new intervening event depends upon the obligation or duty being considered. If the purpose of the legal relationship is to deal with the particular event, then when the actual event occurs it cannot be considered as a new intervening event. It is neither new nor intervening but anticipated even though it may be unusual. This is important in contracts based on risk allocation with force majeure clauses, changed ground conditions clauses or exceptional weather clauses. It is also important in situations where the circumstances raise issues of the duty to warn or the duty to protect against the particular risk event.

2.36   Construction contracts frequently prescribe the responsibility for the consequences of the incidence of particular risk events, even though the events may be described in general terms and the exact nature and extent of the risk event is not specified. This contract risk regime changes the operation of the New Intervening Event concept. The prescribed allocation of risk may create significant problems in ascertaining causation in law. It may be necessary to consider whether or not the initial event increased the chance of the risk event occurring and therefore affected the analysis of causation. The concept of New Intervening Act may not assist in that situation.

2.37   The concept necessarily imports a value judgment based on both the ordinary everyday views of probability as well as the purpose of the legal relationship. In that regard the concept is consistent with the Principled Approach.

The Concept of Intervening Event

2.38   The concept of the New Intervening Event is that the new event is so abnormal and extraordinary, or it is outside the contemplated scope of events to which the legal relationship relates, that it has a causal potency that makes it the sole cause in law of the damage.

2.39   Unlike the "but-for" test, the New Intervening Event concept provides a means of differentiating potency of events. The two examples used in the "but-for" test, together with a further example, demonstrate this.

2.39.1   The traveller's luggage is misdelivered and the subsequent delay leads to the traveller embarking on the doomed SS Titanic[11]. The misdelivery of the luggage is not a causative event at all but simply part of the circumstances that led to embarking on the ship. In any event, the sinking of the SS Titanic is such an abnormal and extraordinary event that it reduces all other events to background. Further, the sinking is outside the scope of events that were contemplated by the legal relationship involved in the delivery of the luggage.

2.39.2   The taxi driver drives too fast and arrives at a point in time and space where a tree falls and injures the passenger[12]. Again, the event of the falling tree is so abnormal and extraordinary, not in the ordinary course of events, that the negligence in driving too fast is simply part of the background. Perhaps more importantly, the event is outside the scope of events contemplated by the law relating to speed limits, which was intended to safeguard against accidents due to speeding and not the incidence of falling trees.

2.39.3   The defendant carries out a promise to direct the way at a crossroads[13]. That in itself is not sufficient to be a cause of the injury. However the situation is different if the direction was given by the defendant in the knowledge that the road was dangerous. In that case, there is a risk that the new event of slipping or being hit by a vehicle might occur to cause the injury, which was assumed by the defendant but not by the claimant. Even in that situation, if the new event that causes the injury is so unusual or out of the ordinary, then the breach simply creates the circumstances for new intervening event.

Judicial Consideration of the Intervening Event Concept

2.40   In *Quinn v Burch Bros Builders Ltd* [1966]CA 2 QB 370 at first instance it was stated that if the injured party, an independent contractor, acted in a way in which a reasonable man would not act, that breaks the chain of causation leading to damage and that the concept of *novus actus interveniens* applied.

---

[11]   The example is taken from Lord Bingham in *Chester v Asfar* [2004] UKHL41.

[12]   The example is taken from Lord Bingham in *Chester v Asfar* [2004] UKHL41.

[13]   The example is taken from *Alexander v Cambridge Credit Corporation* [1987] 9 NSWLR 310.

2.40.1   In the Court of Appeal Quinn argued that the fact that the injured party was negligent was not a *novus actus interveniens*, but that the question of causation is whether the event that happened could have been reasonably foreseen. It was argued that the risk involved was not so enormous or so disproportionate that it was foolishly crazy for Quinn to have undertaken the operation. It was not negligence of such a degree to break the chain of causation.

2.40.2   The Court of Appeal did not accept the argument. The breach of contract by the contractor simply provided the opportunity for the subcontractor to injure himself and in that sense did not cause the injury. Quinn voluntarily and without Burch's knowledge chose to use unsuitable equipment. Quinn realised the risk, but decided to take a chance. There was no term in the contract that Burch should take reasonable care for Burch's safety, although if they had provided equipment it would be a term that the equipment was reasonably safe and suitable for its purpose. Foreseeability might be a useful guide but it was by no means the true criteria for issues of causation.

2.40.3   The basis of the judgment is that even though the actions of Quinn were foreseeable, that was not sufficient. He was being paid on an hourly basis and did not have to act in the way he did. The key appears to be the unnecessary and voluntary assumption of risk by Quinn, without Burch's knowledge, which made his action a new intervening event.

2.41   The principle which applies in the case of human intervention of the injured party has been based on reasonableness or unreasonableness of the claimant's behaviour in determining whether the act was a new intervening act *McKew v Holland & Hannan & Cubitts* [1969] All E.R. 1621.

2.41.1   If a man is injured in such a way that his leg may give way at any moment he must act reasonably and carefully. It is quite possible that in spite of all reasonable care his leg may give way in circumstances such that as a result he sustains further injury. Then that second injury was caused by his disability that in turn was caused by the defender's fault.

2.41.2   However, if the injured man acts unreasonably he cannot hold the defender liable for injury caused by his own unreasonable conduct. His unreasonable conduct is *novus actus interveniens*. The chain of causation has been broken, what follows must be regarded as caused by his own conduct, and not by the defender's fault or the disability caused by it.

2.42   In *Empress Car Company (Abertillery) Ltd. v. National Rivers Authority* [1998]HL the issue was the meaning of the term "cause" in relation to pollution under statute. In that context the general issue of causation was examined.

2.42.1   Lord Hoffmann stated that foreseeability of the act of third parties or natural forces was not the criterion for deciding whether an intervening act caused the damage. People often caused things that they could not have foreseen.

2.42.2   Lord Hoffmann stated that the test for an intervening act distinguished acts and events, which, although not necessarily foreseeable in the particular case, were in the generality a normal and familiar fact of life, and acts or events which were abnormal and extraordinary.

2.42.3   An act or event which is in general terms a normal fact of life might also have been foreseeable in the circumstances of the particular case, but the latter was not necessary for the purposes of liability.

2.42.4   There was nothing extraordinary or abnormal about leaky pipes or lagoons nor anything unusual about people putting unlawful substances into the sewage system nor of ordinary vandalism. When these things happened, they were not an extraordinary coincidence that negatived the causal connection between the original act of accumulating the polluting substance and its escape.

2.42.5   Lord Hoffmann considered that the distinction between ordinary and extraordinary was the common sense criterion to identify intervening acts that negatived causal connection.

2.42.6   Lord Hoffmann recognised that the distinction was one of fact and degree based on common sense.

2.42.7   Lord Clyde stated the principle that applied to intervening events in similar terms to Lord Hoffmann, but recognised that some events may be concurrent causes but in other cases may be the sole cause because they were so far out of the ordinary that the initial event faded into the background.

2.42.8   Lord Clyde considered that foreseeability was not the appropriate test but whether the event was unnatural, extraordinary or of unusual character and that matters of fault or negligence were not immediately relevant.

2.43   In *Reeves v Commissioner of Police of the Metropolis* [2000]HL 1AC360 Lord Jauncey of Tullichettle considered the concept of *novus actus interveniens* in the situation where the police had a duty to take reasonable care to prevent a prisoner who was a known suicide risk from committing suicide. The issue was whether the suicide was a *novus actus interveniens* which negatived the causal connection between the breach of duty and the death. It was clear that the fact that the duty anticipated the event that took place was significant.

2.43.1   An independent act that superseded the effect of the tortuous conduct must relate to an act that was out with the contemplated scope of events to which the duty of care was directed.

2.43.2   Where the duty was specifically directed at the prevention of the occurrence of a certain event, the occurrence of that event could not amount to an independent act breaking the chain of causation from the breach of duty. This was so even if it was unusual for one person to come under a duty to prevent another person deliberately inflicting harm on himself. The duty was directed at that very thing.

2.43.3   Lord Jauncey considered that the defence of *novus actus interveniens* could not assist the commissioner in relation to the admitted breach of duty of care. The deceased's suicide was the precise event to which the duty was directed and as an *actus* it was accordingly neither *novus* nor *interveniens*.

2.43.4   The majority decision of the House of Lords however was that both causes, the free act of the prisoner of sound mind and the breach of duty by the Commissioner, caused the death.

2.44   In *Horton v Taplin Contracts Limited* [2002] EWCACiv1604 the issue was concurrent events in a claim by the employee based on breach of a statutory duty for safety at the work site.

2.44.1   The scaffolding tower did not have outriggers or stabilisers. Whilst Horton was working on the tower, a work colleague "W" toppled the tower over quite deliberately by intentionally applying force with that object in mind. It was argued that the stabilisers would have stopped the scaffolding tower toppling, but there was no expert evidence of the extra force that would have been required and whether it would have been within the physical capacity of W.

2.44.2   The Recorder decided that a mere appeal to common sense was insufficient and the Court of Appeal agreed.

2.44.3   The concept of New Intervening Act was then considered on the assumption that the breach of duty by not providing stabilisers and the actions of W were two causes.

2.44.4   Even if there were two causes, it was still necessary to ask whether the wholly unpredictable, deliberate and violent action of W was an event of such an impact as to obliterate the defendant employer's responsibility. But for that action by W, the accident would not have happened. It was not possible to conclude that but for the lack of stabilisers or guard rails the accident would not have happened.

2.44.5   Even if there were a breach of statutory duty in the failure to supply outriggers and handrails and even if these breaches could properly be considered as having some causative role in the accident, the extraneous deliberate and unpredictable behaviour of W constituted a "new intervening act" such as to break the chain of causation.

2.44.6   It was held that an unforeseeable, unreasonable, deliberate, violent act was a paradigm example of a new intervening event.

2.45   The decision in *Kamilla Hans-Peter Eckhoff KG v AC Oerssleff's EFTF A/B ["The Kamilla"]* [2006]EWHC509 is an application of the principles in *Empress Cars* in a commercial context.

2.45.1   The issue was the extent of liability for damage to cargo due to unseaworthiness under a charter party. The arbitrators had decided that the cargo would not have been rejected but for the unseaworthiness of the vessel. The arbitrators refused to read into the charterparty the concept of foreseeability. The arbitrators decided that unseaworthiness as "a cause" of the loss and that was sufficient.

2.45.2   The owners argued on appeal that by simply applying the "but for" test and ignoring the other facts and in particularly the rejection of the cargo at the port by the Algerian Authorities, the arbitrators had erred in law The term "due" meant "proximate cause" it was argued.

2.45.3   HH Mr Justice Morison held that the test for causation was whether the act or default complained of was a proximate cause of the alleged damage. The "but for" test was appropriate to establish whether there was a causal link between the act or default and the alleged damage. It was a necessary but not sufficient test.

2.45.4   Morison J applied *Empress Cars* that foreseeability was not the criterion for deciding causation. He held that the argument of *novus actus interveniens* was dealt with by the arbitrators when they decided that what happened at the disport was "*by no means unprecedented in our experience*". The unseaworthiness of the vessel and the decision of the Algerian Authority to prohibit the import of the cargo were not mere coincidences.

2.45.5   It was held that the arbitrators had decided that the unseaworthiness was an effective cause of the whole loss, even if some of the loss came as a surprise to the Owners. It was held that the arbitrators had dealt with causation in the way required in law

Application of the Intervening Event Concept to Construction Problems

2.46   The three examples below are used to demonstrate the application of the New Intervening Event Concept to construction problems and compared to the results using the "but-for" test above. The result of the application of the concept of the "Principled Approach" to the examples is detailed in the next Chapter.

Example 1: Concurrent Events – Shortage of Labour & Inclement Weather

2.47   During the period of one weeks delay there is both a shortage of labour and exceptionally adverse weather[14]. Both the event of the shortage of labour and the exceptionally inclement weather operate at the same time to produce the same indivisible damage, one weeks delay. They are independent events.

2.48   The "but-for" test leads to the conclusion that neither event caused the delay and shows the limits of that test.

---

[14]   The first simple example was used by Dyson J in *Henry Boot Construction (UK) Limited v Malmaison Hotel (Manchester) Ltd* [1999]70ConLR32.

2.49   The exceptionally adverse inclement weather by definition is an abnormal and extraordinary event and therefore the concept of New Intervening Event would lead to the conclusion that the exceptionally adverse weather was the sole cause of the one week delay.

2.50   That however is not the end of the test, which also requires the allocation of risk under the particular legal relationship to be considered, in this case the construction contract. If the construction contract deals at all with the allocation of the risk for delay due to exceptionally adverse inclement weather, by say an extension of time clause, then the event cannot be considered a new intervening event. The purpose of the legal relationship is to deal with the particular event, so that when the actual event occurs it cannot be a new intervening event. It is neither new nor intervening but anticipated even though it may be unusual.

2.51   The concept of the New Intervening Event has limited application when a construction contract provides a comprehensive risk allocation regime.   The problem of concurrency remains unresolved.

Example 2: Event During Culpable Delay

2.52   The contractor fails to progress the work as planned and during that period, an event occurs which further interrupts progress[15] The examples below show the limited application of the concept of New Intervening Act. The concept will identify when an independent event breaks the chain of causation but has little to add to the analysis of causation in the case of concurrent events or compound causation.

2.53   Example 2.1: The event is a storm in the period of culpable delay after planned completion that results in flooding of the site and further delay.

    2.53.1   The "but-for" test leads to the conclusion that the event causing the culpable delay caused the damage; the storm would not have had a further effect on progress if the contractor had completed by the contract completion date.

    2.53.2   The storm (and the consequence of flooding), is not in a general sense an intervening event unless it is so unusual or out of the ordinary. Even then, the contract risk regime may affect the application of the concept. The storm is time-dependant and its incidence is therefore related to the contractor-caused culpable delay. The New Intervening Event concept does not lead to a break the chain of causation and does not provide a solution.

2.54   Example 2.2: The contractor's delay is to a part of the works not on the critical path. The storm occurs during the contract period.

    2.54.1   The "but for" test leads again to the conclusion that the event which caused the delay to the part of the works caused the damage.

---

[15]   The second example (slightly modified) was used by Colman J in *Balfour Beatty Building Ltd v Chestermount Properties Ltd* [1993]62BLR1 QBD.

2.54.2   The timing of events in this Example 2 does not change the analysis using the New Intervening Event concept from that in Example 2.1. The New Intervening Event concept does not provide a solution.

2.55   Example 2.3: The event is either an instructed variation or statutory or utility interruption under the contract in a period of culpable delay after planned completion.

2.55.1   The issue of a variation is the exercise of a right of the employer agreed by the parties under the contract. Generally then it is not such an unusual event and out of the ordinary to bring into operation the New Intervening Event concept. Similarly, an exercise of statutory authority is generally normal in construction contracts and again will not involve the concept. It all depends upon the facts, the nature of the works and the terms of the contract.

2.55.2   If the variation/interruption is dependant on the stage of progress of the works, then the "but for" test leads to the conclusion that the additional delay is not caused by the event causing the culpable delay. In contrast, the New Intervening Event concept does not provide a solution. For the reasons above, the concept does not lead to a break the chain of causation and to a sole cause. Variations and statutory/utility interruptions dictated by actual progress are not abnormal or out of the ordinary. Instead, the concept leaves open the cause of further delay between the event causing the contractor's culpable delay and the variation/interruption.

2.55.3   If the variation/interruption is necessary only because of the circumstances created by the culpable delay, then the "but for" test leads to the conclusion that the additional delay was caused by the event causing the culpable delay. Again the New Intervening Event concept does not provide a solution, for the reasons given above, and does not lead to a break in the chain of causation.

2.55.4   If the variation/interruption is independent of the culpable delay the "but-for" test leads to the conclusion that the event causing the culpable delay did not cause the additional delay, but due to concurrency that neither event caused the concurrent period of culpable delay. The New Independent Event concept again does not provide a solution unless the interruption is so abnormal or extraordinary.

Example 3: Event During Extended Period of Contract

2.56   The facts of the example are that a strike occurs during an extended period for completion granted for a variation, which results in further delay due to the shut-down and the seasonal effects on maintenance of equipment[16]

2.57   The "but-for" test leads to the conclusion that the issued variation was the cause of all the further delays.

---

[16]   The third example was used by HH Judge Fox-Andrews QC in *H Fairweather & Co Ltd v London Borough of Wandsworth* [1987]39BLR106 (QBD).

2.58   The event of a strike is different to the storm in Example 2 above. The strike is a political event, the incidence of which cannot be said to naturally increase with the time for construction. It is not in the ordinary course of things time-dependent. A storm on the other hand is time-dependant. The likelihood of a storm will increase with the period of exposure. The strike therefore is an event independent of the extended period

2.59   The strike is a new intervening event since it does not flow naturally from the instructed variation. On this basis, the New Intervening Event concept identifies the strike as the sole cause of the further delay including the seasonal effects since the seasonal effects are a natural consequence of the further delay.

2.60   If the construction contract deals at all with the allocation of the risk for delay due to strikes, by say an extension of time clause, then to the contrary the strike event cannot be considered a new intervening event. It is neither new nor intervening but anticipated even though it may be unusual. In that case, the concept of New Intervening Event does not lead to a sole cause but leaves open the cause of further delay between the event causing the initial delay and the strike.

CHAPTER 3 – THE PRINCIPLED APPROACH

3.1. THE SCOPE OF THE CONCEPT

3.1   The "but-for" test is a concept of causation in fact, but in many cases it is necessary but insufficient to establish causation in law since it is not capable of distinguishing between the legal potency of events.

3.2   The concept of New Intervening Event is an example of the Principled Approach since it requires value judgments, but provides a solution to causation in law only in one particular situation.

3.3   The central premise of the concept of the Principled Approach is that causation in law requires value judgments and is not simply a matter of logical and scientific analysis. The value judgments required to establish causation in law involve consideration of the legal issues, risk and probabilities.

   3.3.1   The probability of the event causing the damage.

   3.3.2   The allocation of risk between the Claimant and the Defendant, including the assumption of risk by either of them.

   3.3.3   The legal rule, principle of law, duty or obligation which governs the relationship between the Claimant and Defendant.

   3.3.4   The justice or fairness in determining that the Claimant should be considered liable in law for the cause of the damage.

3.4   Establishing causation in law depends upon the evidence in the particular case. The concept of the burden of proof deals with the evidence required to establish entitlement. "Burden of proof" involves similar concepts of probabilities based on the evidence, but it is a separate and distinct concept from causation in law.

3.5   The concept of the burden of proof allows an inference to be made based on conflicting evidence based on the probability of occurrence. If the burden of proof is discharged, then a fact which is uncertain is treated as certain, Lord Diplock in *Mallett v McMonagle* [1970] AC 166

3.6   If the burden of proving the conditions for causation is not discharged then the question of causation will not arise at all.

3.7   The Defendant may be considered to have caused the damage in law even though it is not possible to prove that the Defendant is the only participant who has in fact caused the damage. In some situations, the Court will draw an inference that the event the responsibility of the Defendant made a material contribution to the damage because he significantly increased the risk of damage.

3.8   In providing a common sense answer to a question of causation in order to allocate liability, it is necessary to consider the particular obligation or duty and its scope and purpose *Empress Car Company (Abertillery) Ltd. v. National Rivers Authority* [1998]HL. Extending the principle to construction contracts, a different answer to the issue of causation may result in relation to different obligations and different kinds of damage. The common situation is where the contractor has failed to complete by the specified completion date and there are multiple possible causes of the delay. The view of legal causation for the delay may differ when considering an employer's claim for liquidated damages as opposed to the contractor's claim for prolongation costs, even though the delay period is the same.

3.9   Causation in law does not itself establish liability or the extent of liability. Even if an event is a cause in law, it is still necessary to establish that the event arises from a breach of duty or legal obligation that gives rise to liability.

3.10   Causation in law does not itself establish the measure of damage, which is dealt with by the concept of remoteness of damage, which is related but distinct from causation in law.

3.11   When based on probability in the context of the multiplicity of causes, the Principled Approach leads logically to the apportionment of damages. This differs from the measure of damages.

3.2. BURDEN OF PROOF

3.12   A necessary first step is to prove the facts of the necessary conditions of causation and then the fact of causation by the Defendant In construction cases this may be particularly difficult when there are frequently multiple events and participants and it is not usually possible to assemble all the facts.

   3.12.1   If the necessary facts for the conditions for causation are not proved then the issue of causation in law does not arise.

   3.12.2   If the evidence does not allow the inference to be drawn that the necessary facts for causation occurred, then the Defendant did not cause the damage.

3.13   Since both the concepts of burden of proof and causation in law involve assessments of probabilities, the conclusion in each case must be consistent.

3.14   It is only in exceptional situations that a disputed issue of fact will be decided on the basis of the failure to discharge the burden of proof, but instead the facts will usually be inferred from the evidence.

3.15   The basic propositions of proof of evidence in relation to causation are demonstrated by three cases below.

3.16   The first case was the judgment of the House of Lords in *Rhesa Shipping Co SA v Edmunds and Another (The Popi M)* [1985] 2 All ER 712. The issue was whether the shipowners were entitled to claim under an insurance policy for the total loss of a ship.

3.16.1　The ship had sunk because of the entry of water through a large aperture in the hull shell plating. Competing theories of the events causing the loss were postulated. The plaintiff shipowners discounted a number of possible events and relied a possible collision by a submerged submarine. The defendant underwriters contended that prolonged wear and tear had caused the plates to open under the ordinary action of wind and wave but by a doubtful mechanism. The judge at first instance adopted the submarine theory even though he considered it extremely improbable.

3.16.2　Lord Brandon in the House of Lords referred to the non-judicial dictum described by the fictional character Sherlock Holmes that "... *when you have eliminated the impossible, whatever remains, however improbable, must be the truth*". It was held that it was inappropriate to apply that dictum to the process of fact-finding that a judge was to perform. The dictum could only be applied when all relevant facts were known, so that all possible explanations, except the extremely improbable one, could properly be eliminated.

3.16.3　Lord Brandon held that in any event the legal concept of proof of a case on a balance of probabilities must be applied with common sense. A finding that an event is more likely to have occurred than not, does not accord with common sense if a judge also finds that the occurrence of an event is extremely improbable.

3.16.4　It was held that the judge at first instance had adopted an erroneous approach by regarding himself as compelled to choose between two theories, both of which he regarded as extremely improbable, or one of which he regarded as extremely improbable and the other of which he regarded as virtually impossible. In these circumstances, the Judge should have found that the true cause of loss was in doubt and that the shipowners had failed to discharge the burden of proof.

3.16.5　It was held that it is always open to the Court even after prolonged enquiry with a mass of expert evidence to conclude that the proximate cause of the damage (in this case the loss of the ship) even on the balance of probabilities was in doubt. In cases in which the evidence is unsatisfactory, deciding on the burden of proof may be the only just course for the judge to take.

3.17　The approach to be adopted is one based on the evidence as demonstrated in the second case of *Datec Electronics Holdings Ltd v United Parcels Service Limited* [2005] EWCA Civ 1418[17], a carriage of goods case.

---

[17]　On appeal to the House of Lords in *Datec Electronics Holdings Limited v United Parcels Service Limited [2007] UKHL 23*, Lord Justice Mance giving leading judgment observed that what had been in issue in the Court of Appeal was the inferences with regard to the causation of loss to be drawn from primary facts which are not in dispute. He found the reasons given by Richards LJ for reversing the judge compelling and the appeal was dismissed.

3.17.1 Whichever account was the least improbable still has to be evaluated against the surrounding realities. It was not necessary to know all the facts, but the court must be able to make findings on all matters of fact which call for inquiry in resolving the issue before it.

3.17.2 It was held that Lord Brandon's appeal to common sense in *The Popi M* was not that judges could or should disbelieve evidence that an event has occurred simply because its occurrence was highly improbable. It was observed that the law, like life, was littered with highly improbable events, many of them defying common sense, which had nevertheless indubitably happened. Lord Brandon was considering an occurrence which, albeit the least improbable of those canvassed, made little or no intrinsic sense. It was observed that such cases might fail for want of sufficient proof.

3.17.3 In the particular case, it was found that there was sufficient evidence to enable the Court to engage in an informed analysis of the possible causes of the loss of goods and to reach a reasoned conclusion as to the probable cause. It was held that the fact that the experts were unable to reach a conclusion of their own on the fate of the packages did not preclude the court from reaching such a conclusion on the totality of the evidence and in the light of the findings of fact. In that case, the established facts greatly reduced the scope for uncertainty, and the inferences that could be drawn from them as to the condition of the packages and assessment of the fate of the packages.

3.17.4 Importantly there was detailed consideration at the trial of all possible explanations for the loss. It was not suggested that there might exist any realistic possibility that the experts had failed to canvass. The court had been able to look closely at the evidence for and against each of the possible explanations.

3.17.5 Significantly, the Court of Appeal considered that some of the explanations for the loss were implausible based on the evidence, such as theft by a third party or accidental loss. The remaining possibility was theft by UPS employees. The Court of Appeal considered that the judges finding of accidental loss was implausible and improbable and that the explanation of employee theft fitted well with the facts even though the employees could not be identified.

3.17.6 It was held that there was no inconsistency between the approach of the Court of Appeal and the observations of Lord Brandon in *The Popi M*. The conclusion of the probable cause of the loss as employee theft was not based on a process of elimination of the impossible, in application of the dictum of Sherlock Holmes. Instead, it took into consideration the relative probabilities or improbabilities of various possible causes as part of the overall process of reasoning. Employee theft was a plausible explanation and very far from being an extremely improbable event. A finding that employee theft was more likely than not to have been the cause of loss accorded perfectly well with common sense.

3.18   The situations in which a disputed issue of fact is to be decided by resort to the concept of burden of proof were examined by the Court of Appeal in the third case of *Stephens v Cannon* [2005] EWCA Civ 222 in which the propositions of law were stated.

   3.18.1   The issue was the valuation of a property based on the conflicting evidence of two experts; a similar situation is common in construction. In the first instance decision, the Master had been unable to choose between the valuations. He decided on the basis of the Claimant's failure to discharge the burden of proof and adopted the defendant's valuation.

   3.18.2   The Court of Appeal held that the Master should not have asked which valuation he should accept, but what in the light of the evidence of the two experts was the probable value of the property and adjudicated on the specific differences between each valuation.

   3.18.3   The Court of Appeal held that only in exceptional circumstances should a dispute of fact be decided on the basis of the concept of burden of proof. It was only if a tribunal could not reasonably make a finding in relation to a disputed issue, despite striving to do so, that it should decide on the basis of failure to discharge the burden of proof. A detailed demonstration and explanation of the endeavour must be set out in the reasons for the decision unless readily inferred from the circumstances.

3.3. INDIVISIBLE DAMAGE – JOINT AND SEVERAL LIABILITY

3.19   An example of the Principled Approach is the rule of joint and several liability in the situation of indivisible damage by joint events.

3.20   Devlin J gave an example in *Dingle v Associated Newspapers Ltd* [1961] 2 QB 162 of indivisible damage of several actions causing injury to a plaintiff and leading to a loss of earnings as a result.

   3.20.1   He considered that if it was possible to separate the particular damage caused by each action, then liability for those parts could be allocated. Where however the damage was indivisible, in the example the loss of earnings, then the defendant was liable for the whole.

   3.20.2   If four men, acting severally and not in concert, struck the plaintiff one after another and as a result of his injuries he suffered shock and was detained in hospital and lost a month's wages, each wrongdoer was liable to compensate for the whole loss of earnings.

   3.20.3   If there were four distinct physical injuries, each man would be liable only for the consequences peculiar to the injury he inflicted, but in the example the loss of earnings was one injury caused in part by all four defendants.

3.20.4   It was essential for this purpose that the loss should be one and indivisible; whether it was so or not was a matter of fact and not a matter of law.

3.21   The situation shows the limits of the "but for" test to causation in law. In the case of indivisible damage caused by joint events, by definition the damage will still occur in the absence of one of the events from the circumstances.

3.22   The Principled Approach adopts a rule of joint and several liability and finds causation in law between the Claimant and the Defendant if the event the responsibility of the Defendant is "a" material cause of the damage. It does not need to be the sole cause. There is no unfairness to the Defendant since he can seek contribution from the joint contributors in further actions. It must be clear that the event the responsibility of the Defendant was a proximate cause of the damage.

3.23   The principle of joint and several liability was stated by Devlin LJ in *Dingle v Associated Newspapers Ltd* [1961] 2 QB 162:

3.23.1   Where injury has been done to the plaintiff and the injury is indivisible, any tortfeasor whose act has been a proximate cause of the injury must compensate for the whole of it.

3.23.2   As between the plaintiff and the defendant, it is immaterial that there are others whose acts also have been a cause of the injury and it does not matter whether those others have or have not a good defence.

3.23.3   These factors would be relevant in a claim between tortfeasors for contribution, but the plaintiff is not concerned with that; he can obtain judgment for total compensation from anyone whose act has been a cause of his injury.

3.23.4   If there is more than one of such persons, it is immaterial to the plaintiff whether they are joint tortfeasors or not.

3.24   The principle of joint and several liability indirectly allows apportionment of the damage, not between the Claimant and Defendant, but between the joint contributors. The concept may apply where the joint contributors are independent of the Claimant but contracted to him. In that situation the Principled Approach is to apply the concepts in the rule of joint and several liability, and establish causation in law if the event the responsibility of the Defendant is "a" material cause of the damage even though the Claimant's other contractors also contributed to the damage. The Defendant can seek contribution from the other contractors.

3.25   That was the situation in *Great Eastern Hotel Company Ltd v John Laing Construction Ltd* [2005] EWHC 181 (TCC).

3.25.1   GEH claimed damages from Laing for breaches of a Construction Management Agreement and the issue was the amounts paid to and the actions of, the professional team and Trade Contractors who carried out the work.

3.25.2   HH David Wilcox held that in the absence of provisions to the contrary the appropriate test was that if a party proved the breach and the proven breach materially contributed to the loss then it could recover the whole loss, even if there was another effective contributory cause provided that there was no double recovery.

3.25.3   This approach caused no injustice, because the Defendant who pays is protected, because it was open to him to seek contribution from any other contract breaker.

3.26   The principle of joint and several liability does not apply in the situation where the multiple events are the responsibility of one or both parties to the construction contract, and no third party is involved. In that situation, there may be several but not joint liability and more direct apportionment may be necessary. The contract terms may prescribe the potency of concurrent events in relation to the particular damage and compensation.

3.27   As observed in *Great Eastern Hotel Company Ltd v John Laing Construction Ltd* [2005] EWHC 181 (TCC) each claim or group of claims must be examined on their own facts and in the context of the specific contractual provisions which may give rise to a consideration of the comparative potency of causal events and to apportionment.

3.4. RISK, LOSS OF CHANCE AND PROBABILITIES

The Principled Approach – A General Theory from Hard Cases

3.28   The Principled Approach to the issue of causation is demonstrated in the recent developments of the law in personal injury in relation to the condition known as mesothelioma. The condition is an invariably fatal cancer of the lining of the lungs or abdomen of which the only known cause is the inhalation of asbestos fibres. The latency period of the disease is in many cases extremely long which combined with the uncertainty as to the mechanism of carcinogenicity has created hard cases.

3.29   Although the law is in personal injury, nonetheless the development provides a coherent structured principle of causation in law. It is precisely because the law has been developed in hard cases that the principles of causation in law so derived can be considered to be a general theory of causation in law.

3.30   The value judgments that are made in the cases and the public policy considerations will differ in other areas of law, but the principle of using value judgments does not.

Proving the Conditions of Causation

3.31   If the burden of proving the conditions for causation is not discharged then the question of causation will not arise at all. This is particularly relevant where the allegation is an omission or failure to act. In that case, a necessary condition of causation is that the omitted act is capable of having any effect at all. That will depend upon the actual situation when the act should have taken place.

3.32   In the medical negligence case of *Hotson v East Berkshire HA* [1987] HL the two events were first a fall in which Hotson sustained a hip injury and second the hospital's delay in providing proper treatment.

    3.32.1   Lord Brandon recognized the difficulties when there were doubts as to the effect that proper treatment would have had in avoiding the long-term effects of the accident. It is implicit in the judgment that an action could create liability if it affected the risk of a particular result occurring.

    3.32.2   If the issue was whether a patient's condition was such that proper treatment could affect a particular result then it was to be determined on the balance of probabilities.

    3.32.3   One way of describing that balance was to say that there was at that time a sufficient chance that the particular result could be attained to justify holding that the loss of that result was caused by the absence of proper treatment.

    3.32.4   The fundamental question of fact was the condition of the patient before the proper treatment should have started. There was no issue of a hypothetical state of facts.

    3.32.5   It was found as a fact that at the time when proper treatment should have been given, there was no chance of avoiding the long term consequences of the accident so that the lack of such treatment did not cause the loss of chance of avoiding the long-term consequences.

    3.32.6   The House rejected the approach of awarding a proportionate fraction of the full damages to compensate for the injury as the measure of damages for the lost chance. Hotson failed on causation so no question of quantification arose.

Risk and Probability

3.33   The House of Lord's decision in *Hotson v East Berkshire HA* [1987] HL was based on the standard rule that it must be proved on a balance of probability that the defendant's conduct did cause the damage in the sense that it affected the risk of occurrence of the damage. However where the injury is indivisible, but difficulties of proving causation would create injustice, the law has developed an exception to the general rule in medical negligence cases based on probability of causation. The importance of the development to construction law is the recognition of the concepts of allocation of risk and probabilities in issues of causation based on justice and fairness and not simply application of causal requirement rules.

3.34   In *Fairchild v Glenhaven Funeral Services Ltd [2002] UKHL 22;* [2003] 1 AC 32 Fairchild contracted mesothelioma by exposure to asbestos dust at his workplace while working for one or other of his employers.

3.34.1   Prolonged exposure to asbestos increases the risk of mesothelioma, but only in a statistical sense. The disease might be caused by inhalation of a single fibre of asbestos which operated in a way that medical science did not fully understand, in the transformation of a normal mesothelial cell into a malignant tumour. Accordingly, mesothelioma was an indivisible injury.

3.34.2   It was not possible by any known medical science to identify which of the employers had been Fairchild's employer when he had inhaled the asbestos fibres that caused the disease. Nor was it possible by any known medical science to eliminate any employer from those who might have been the employer at the relevant time. On the other hand, the expert medical evidence did justify the conclusion that his employer at the relevant time must have been one, and may have been more than one, of the employers.

3.34.3   Mrs Fairchild was unable to prove on any balance of probabilities which employer's breach of duty had caused her husband's mesothelioma. On a traditional approach, the standard rule is that it is not enough to show that the defendant's conduct might have caused the damage. It must be proved on a balance of probability that the defendant's conduct did cause the damage.

3.34.4   The House of Lords remedied the evident unfairness of the situation by expanding the boundaries of liability in tort and creating an exception to the general rule. They built on the earlier decision of the House of Lords in *McGhee v National Coal Board* [1973] 1 WLR 1.

3.34.5   No distinction was made between making a material contribution to causing the disease and materially increasing the risk of his contracting it. Liability was imposed on the past employer even though they may not have caused the damage but simply because they had materially contributed to the risk of causing that damage.

3.34.6   Lord Bingham concluded that it was just and in accordance with commonsense to treat the conduct of A and B in exposing C to a risk to which he should not have been exposed as making a material contribution to the contracting by C of a condition against which it was the duty of A and B to protect him.

3.34.7   Accordingly, it was decided that the employer was jointly and severally liable if it had materially and tortuously contributed to the risk of producing mesothelioma, without the need to prove direct causation of the condition.

Apportionment

3.35   The difficulties of the exception in *Fairchild* in a case where it was possible that the injured party may himself have caused the indivisible injury, was resolved by the introduction of apportionment in the probability analysis of causation in the House of Lords judgment in *Barker v St Gobain Pipelines plc* [2006]UKHL20.

3.35.1 Barker died of asbestos-related mesothelioma. Just like the facts in *Fairchild* there had been exposure to asbestos due to breaches of duty by past employers. The difference with *Fairchild* was that Barker was also exposed due to his own failure to take reasonable care for his own safety while as a self-employed plasterer. Unlike the facts of *Fairchild*, not all the exposures which could have caused the disease involved breaches of duty to the claimant or were within the control of a defendant.

3.35.2 Since the injury of asbestos related mesothelioma is an indivisible injury, the issue was whether the employer was jointly and severally liable for all the damage on the basis of *Fairchild* or only a proportion.

3.35.3 The House of Lords took the approach of characterising the damage as the risk of contracting mesothelioma and refusing to apply the rule on joint and several liability where liability was on the basis that a party *might* have caused the damage.

3.35.4 Lord Hoffmann held that in that situation apportionment according to probabilities was the fair approach.

3.35.5 The attribution of liability according to the relative degree of contribution to the chance of the disease being contracted was considered to smooth the roughness of the justice which a rule of joint and several liability created.

3.35.6 The defendant should not be allowed to escape liability altogether, but he should not be liable for more than the damage which he caused. Since this was a case in which science could deal only in probabilities, the law should accept that position and attribute liability according to probabilities.

3.35.7 The justification for the joint and several liability rule was that if you caused harm, there is no reason why your liability should be reduced because someone else also caused the same harm.

3.35.8 When liability was exceptionally imposed because the plaintiff might have caused harm, the same considerations did not apply. Fairness suggested that if more than one person might have been responsible, liability should be divided according to the probability that one or other caused the harm.

3.35.9 Lord Walker made clear that liability was allocated on the basis of the proportion of the risk caused by the defendant. Although damage was indivisible, risk was not.

3.35.10 Baroness Hale recognised that there were limits to the rule of joint and several liability. It did not automatically apply where there was indivisible damage. She recognised that the law had to keep pace with the development of probabilistic theories of causation and the apportionment of risk.

3.35.11 Baroness Hale recognised that the concept of causation was being developed and that the apportionment of liability was a policy decision that depended on the availability of a sensible basis for apportionment. The issue was one of fairness.

3.35.12 Baroness Hale recognised that the defendants might have caused no damage at all. The reason for allocating liability was that it was fair that the defendants should make some contribution. The measure was in proportion to the contribution to the risk of damage occurring.

3.35.13 The House of Lords remitted the case to the High Court to redetermine the damages by reference to the proportion of the risk attributable to the breach of duty.

Statutory Joint and Several Liability

3.36 The House of Lords judgment in *Barker v St Gobain Pipelines plc* [2006]UKHL20 was that where the Claimant <u>might</u> have contributed to the damage that the wrongdoing was several and not joint, with the result that recovery had to be proportioned to each defendant's relative contribution to the chance of the person contracting the disease.

3.37 The doctrine was reversed by Section 3 of the Compensation Act 2006, so that in mesothelioma cases each contributory wrongdoer is liable for the whole of the damage, a form of statutory joint and several liability, but still has the right to recover contribution from other tortfeasors.

3.38 The explanatory memorandum for the Joint Committee on Statutory Instruments identified the policy background for the change in law, to reverse the consequences of the House of Lord's judgment so that victims would not be burdened with the requirement to find all possible negligent persons in order to obtain full compensation[18].

3.39 The above developments of law are recognition of the role of probability and risk allocation in the analysis of causation in law. It is clear that fairness may require resort to more flexible concepts than joint and several liability. Apportionment of liability in proportion to the change in risk caused by the Claimant and the Defendant may be appropriate in some situations. The issue of fairness may however involve particular policy considerations. In construction contracts, the expectation of the parties and the express allocation of risk are likely to be a paramount consideration.

---

[18] Explanatory Memorandum to the Compensation Act 2006 (Contribution for Mesothelioma Claims) Regulations 2006 No 3259.

Proof of Breach of Duty

3.40   Causation in law does not itself establish liability or the extent of liability. Even if an event is a cause in law, it is still necessary to establish that the event arises from a breach of duty or legal obligation that gives rise to liability.

3.41   In *Brett v University of Reading* [2007] EWCACiv88 the Court of Appeal again had to consider liability for the Claimant contracting mesothelioma.

　　3.41.1   Brett had a working life between 1940 and 1999 in engineering and construction work. There was a real possibility that he had been exposed in many of these jobs to airborne asbestos. No other employer was sued except the University of Reading.

　　3.41.2   It was recognised that the two overlapping questions were (i) had the Defendant made any contribution to the risk that had eventuated, and (ii) if so, was the Defendant legally at fault. The judge at first instance conflated the separate issues of contribution and fault. The critical question was whether the exposure to which it was likely that Brett was subjected was such as to put the University in breach of its duties to him. It was for the Claimant to establish the elements of its case.

　　3.41.3   It was found that although the evidence was sufficient to infer that Brett came into contact with asbestos in the course of his work at Reading University, it was not sufficient to show, or to support the inference, that the University had failed to take the necessary steps to protect him from inhaling it. The fact of developing mesothelioma could not fill the gap, because for most of his life Brett had been in jobs that were capable of bringing him into contact with airborne asbestos.

　　3.41.4   It was held that Brett had failed to prove a breach of duty by the University.

3.5. INDIVISIBLE DAMAGE – SEPARATE CAUSES, GENERAL PRINCIPLE IN CONSTRUCTION LAW

Summary – Proof, Principles and Value Judgments

3.42   Issues of causation in construction can raise complicated issues of fact. As described above and repeated below the requirements for proof of facts and the place of causation in establishing liability are in summary:

　　3.42.1   The necessary facts for the conditions for causation must be proved otherwise the issue of causation in law does not arise.

　　3.42.2   Evidence must be adduced to allow the inference to be drawn that the necessary facts for causation occurred; otherwise, the Defendant did not cause the damage.

3.42.3 Even if an event is a cause in law, it is still necessary to establish that the event arises from a breach of duty or legal obligation that gives rise to liability.

3.42.4 Causation in law does not itself establish the measure of damage, which is dealt with by the related concept of remoteness of damage.

3.43 The Principled Approach is not expressly referred to in any decided cases in construction law, but explains the reasoning of a number of cases. The Principled Approach requires value judgments in respect of the following:

3.43.1 The probability of the event causing the damage.

3.43.2 The allocation of risk between the Claimant and the Defendant, including the assumption of risk by either of them.

3.43.3 The legal rule, principle of law, duty or obligation which governs the relationship between the Claimant and Defendant.

3.43.4 The justice or fairness in determining that the Claimant should be considered liable in law for the cause of the damage.

3.44 When based on probability in the context of the multiplicity of causes, the Principled Approach leads to the apportionment of damages, which is different to the measure of damages.

Proof of Conditions of Causation

3.45 The damage often in issue is the delay to completion of the contract works argued as caused by several events. Even if it can be proved that the event occurred, the issue of causation will not arise if the event could not have affected the completion of the works.

3.46 In *Balfour Beatty Building Ltd v Chestermount Properties Ltd* [1993]62BLR1 QBD the contract was substantially in the JCT Standard Form 1980, Private Edition with Approximate Quantities. The JCT form of contract lists the "Relevant Events" which entitle a contractor to extensions of time.

3.47 As described further below Colman J established the principles that apply in construction law, but observed that if the Relevant Event had no effect on progress, no extension of time was due. His approach was to give effect to the allocation of risk regime, but considered that the requirement to satisfy the necessary initial condition did not affect the agreed allocation of risk, although he did not express his decision in those terms. The Relevant Event he was required to consider was an instructed variation.

3.47.1 If the variation works could reasonably be conducted simultaneously with the original works without interfering with their progress and were unlikely to prolong practical completion, the architect might properly conclude that no extension of time was justified. He would therefore leave the completion date where it was.

3.47.2   The contractor would pay liquidated damages for the amount of time by which he had exceeded the original period of time for completion.

3.47.3   The contractor's continuing liability to pay liquidated damages while he was carrying out the variation works did not reflect an assumption by him of the risk of loss of time due to what would otherwise be an act of prevention. It merely reflected the contractor's breach of contract by failing to complete the original works within the contract period for completion.

3.48   This aspect of the approach by Colman J was developed in the decision in the construction case *Henry Boot Construction (UK) Limited v Malmaison Hotel (Manchester) Ltd* [1999] which emphasises the need to prove the conditions of causation.

3.48.1   The contract was the JCT Standard Form of Building Contract with Quantities, 1980 Edition, also incorporating the sectional completion supplement. The case was an appeal from the decision of an arbitrator in the circumstances where Malmaison had deducted £250,000 of liquidated damages for 10 weeks delay. Henry Boot contested the extension of time granted. The matter before Mr Justice Dyson was whether or not the arbitrator had jurisdiction to consider matters raised by Malmaison as causing delay in addition to the Relevant Events identified by Henry Boot. The issue therefore was the contractor's obligation to complete by a specified date and the employer's right to liquidated damages and not a claim by the contractor for additional costs or loss and expense.

3.48.2   Dyson J held that a contractor was not entitled to an extension of time simply because there was a Relevant Event, but an initial condition had to be met. The first step was to examine whether or not a Relevant Event had any effect at all on actual progress. The approach by Mr Justice Dyson was to distinguish between a Relevant Event which was truly concurrent with other events and a Relevant Event that was not. In that respect as a matter of principle, it is similar in reasoning to the approach to the issue of causation in the medical negligence case of *Hotson v East Berkshire HA* [1987] HL above, where an event that did not affect the risk of damage was not a cause in law of the damage.

3.48.3   It was held that the employer was entitled to say that a Relevant Event was not likely to or did not cause delay because it was not on the critical path to completion and to advance a positive case for the cause of the actual delay.

3.49   The initial requirement to ascertain whether or not a Relevant Events has any effect on the completion of the works was confirmed in *The Royal Brompton Hospital NHS Trust v Watkins Gray International* [2000] QBD (TCC) *ConLR148*. The issue in that case was whether or not the Architect had been negligent in deciding the extension of time.

3.49.1   His Honour Judge Richard Seymour QC emphasised that the first step in examining an extension of time under the JCT Form was to establish that the Relevant Event caused or was likely to cause delay to the completion date. If the Relevant Event did not have that effect, then there was no issue of concurrency.

3.49.2 Seymour J said that events were not operating concurrently in a situation in which work was already delayed by for example the contractor's shortage of labour and a Relevant Event occurs which, had the contractor not been delayed, would have caused him to be delayed, but which in fact, by reason of the existing delay, made no difference. In such a situation although there is a Relevant Event, the completion of the Works is not likely to be delayed beyond the Completion Date. The Relevant Event simply has no effect upon the completion date as shown diagrammatically below in Figure 1.

Figure 1 - Proof of Necessary Condition

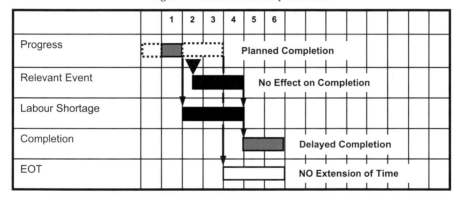

3.49.3 Seymour J distinguished that situation from one where the works are proceeding in a regular fashion and on programme, when two things happen, either of which, had it happened on its own, would have caused delay, and one is a Relevant Event while the other is not. In such circumstances, he considered there was a real concurrency of causes of the delay.

3.50 The above test to satisfy the conditions for causation defines concurrency as two events occurring at the same time and distinguishes two events occurring at different times. The test uses the time difference to distinguish between an operating event and a coincidental event that has no real effect. The timing of the two events of itself is not the universal significant characteristic to satisfy the condition of causation.

3.51 Only in the situation where the Relevant Event and the shortage of labour in the example affect the same activity, is the time difference the important characteristic. The contractor has already allowed, or put in train, the event of not providing sufficient labour so as to delay the activity. The Relevant Event simply occurs in the context of the operating event of the shortage of labour. The fact of the time difference, allows that conclusion to be made so that the issue of causation in law does not arise.

3.52 In the situation where the Relevant Event and the shortage of labour do not affect the same activity, then the fact of the time difference may not allow that conclusion to be made. If at the time of the events the activity affected by the Relevant Event is not on the critical path then the initial conclusion is that the Relevant Event did not affect completion.

3.53 This is shown below diagrammatically in Figure 2, which shows two activities one of which is on the critical path and the other is not.

Figure 2 - Separate Events Affecting Different Activities at Date of Activity

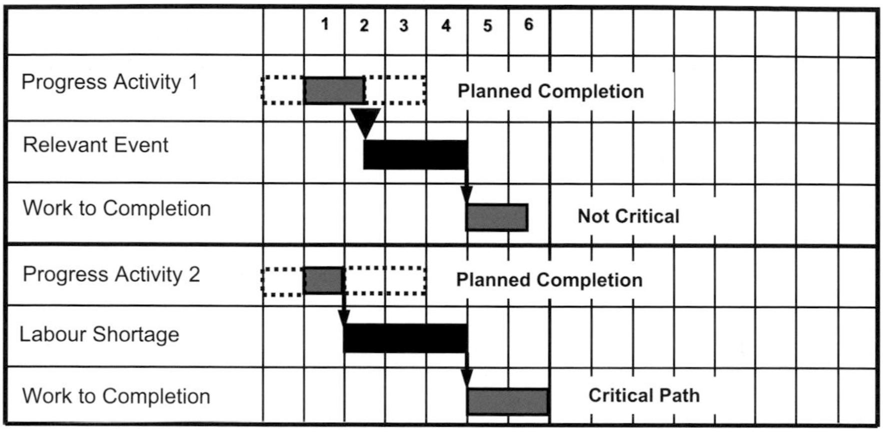

3.54 The initial conclusion needs to be verified by examination of actual progress to completion. The initial conclusion is only correct if the critical path does not change during the progress of the works. If viewed retrospectively progress is such that the activity affected by the Relevant Event is on the critical path and the event affected by shortage of labour is not, then the timing difference is not sufficient to draw the conclusion that the Relevant Event occurred in the context of the shortage of labour.

3.55 This is shown below diagrammatically in Figure 3.

Figure 3 - Separate Events Affecting Different Activities at Completion

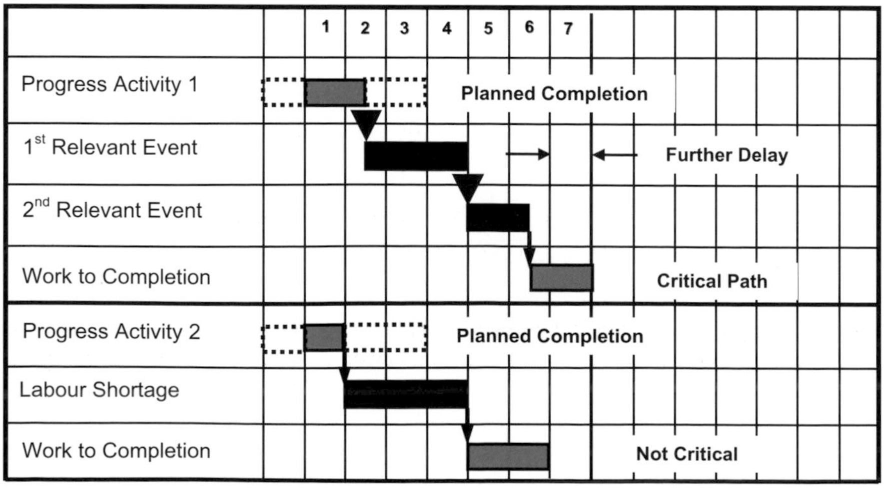

3.56   Figure 3 above shows that a Relevant Event, which was not on the critical path to completion when it occurred, is on the actual critical path at completion due to the incidence of a subsequent Relevant Event.

3.57   In the above case, it cannot be said that the timing difference of the two events of the first Relevant Event and shortage of labour shows that the first Relevant Event could not have affected the completion date. This remains the case even if both events are on separate critical paths or "near" critical paths. In those cases, the proper conclusion is that the condition for causation is satisfied and that the issue of causation in law must then be considered.

Example 1 – Employer's Claim for Damages for Delay

3.58   If the initial condition is satisfied, the approach to be applied when there are concurrent events and the damage claimed is the Employer's time related loss was established by Colman J in *Balfour Beatty Building Ltd v Chestermount Properties Ltd* [1993]62BLR1 QBD.

3.59   The approach was common ground in *Henry Boot Construction (UK) Limited v Malmaison Hotel (Manchester) Ltd* [1999].

    3.59.1   Mr Justice Dyson accepted the approach as a statement of law without adverse comment.

    3.59.2   It was agreed that if there are two concurrent causes of delay, one of which is a Relevant Event, and the other is not, then the contractor was entitled to an extension of time for the period of delay caused by the Relevant Event notwithstanding the concurrent effect of the other event.

    3.59.3   The approach was demonstrated by an example, which has been examined above as Example 1 in which the two events were the Relevant Event under the JCT Form of exceptionally inclement weather and the event of shortage of labour the fault of the contractor.

    3.59.4   In the example, the Architect was required to grant an extension of time of one week, if the failure to work during that week was likely to delay the Works beyond the Completion Date by one week and if it was fair and reasonable to do so.

    3.59.5   The Architect could not refuse to grant an extension of time on the grounds that the delay would have occurred in any event by reason of the shortage of labour.

3.60   Example 1 is shown diagrammatically below in Figure 4. The two events are shown as being co-extensive in time and both causing the same indivisible damage of delay to completion.

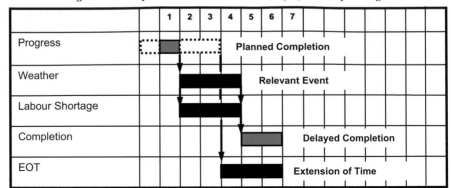

Figure 4 - Example 1 - Concurrent Events - Employers Delay Damages

3.61   The approach taken by Mr Justice Dyson is not the application of a factual causation concept since he clearly rejected the "but for" test as grounds for refusing an extension of time. As described above the available tests for causation are of little assistance in cases of concurrency.

       3.61.1   As examined above for Example 1, in the case of concurrent events each attributable to one of the Parties, the indivisibility of damage means that the "but-for" test is inadequate as a test for establishing causation.

       3.61.2   As examined above for Example 1, the concept of the New Intervening Event has limited application when a construction contract provides a comprehensive risk allocation regime. The problem of concurrency remains unresolved using the New Intervening Event concept.

3.62   Mr Justice Dyson decided causation in law on the basis of the allocation of risk under the contract as defined by the list of Relevant Events, using the principled approach of Colman J.

Value Judgment of Allocation of Risk – Employer's Claim for Damages for Delay

3.63   In *Balfour Beatty Building Ltd v Chestermount Properties Ltd* [1993] 62 BLR 1 Balfour Beatty was challenging Chestermount's right to deduct £3.84m in liquidated damages. Colman J was required to consider the contractual system of the obligation to complete by a specified date, the provisions for extension of time and the right to levy liquidated damages. The Relevant Event was an instructed variation.

       3.63.1   The approach taken by Colman J recognised that superimposed on the obligation to complete and the right to liquidated damages for failure to do so, was a system of allocation of risk and that the extension of time provisions were intended to give effect to that agreed risk allocation. He recognised that this approach might lead to an extension of time such that the extended completion date was before the actual date of the instructed variation. He dealt with this apparent factual peculiarity and the question whether this was contrary to common sense by emphasising the system of allocation of risk.

3.63.2 Colman J approached the matter of causation, not on the basis of the application of factual causal concepts, but on the basis of whether it was fair in the circumstances for the contractor to be liable for liquidated damages for a period of delay. The agreed allocation of risk was central to the approach. The operation of the extension of time provisions was measured against this principle in order to determine the level of damages for delay for which the contractor should be considered liable.

3.63.3 The underlying objective was to arrive at the aggregate period of time within which the contract works as ultimately defined **ought to have been completed** having regard to the incidence of non-contractor's risk events. The architect was required to calculate the extent to which the completion of the works had exceeded that period.

3.63.4 The language used by Colman J was in terms of risk events and fair allocation of liability. The extension of time was required to be determined to fix the contractor's obligation to complete so that the apportionment of risk under the contract was given effect. If it was otherwise the extension of time would make the contractor liable in liquidated damages for events which were not the contractor's risk.

3.63.5 Colman J observed that it would require clear words to depart from the requirement to fix an extension of time of a period co-extensive with the delay caused by the Relevant Event, given the purpose of the regimes of obligation to complete, extension of time provisions and liquidated damages.

3.64 It is implicit in the observations of Colman J that it is possible to provide a different risk regime by clear provisions of the contract dealing with concurrency. Nonetheless, it will be difficult for the Employer to construct a risk regime that allows the deduction of liquidated damages when there are concurrent events causing delay, without the provision being construed as a penalty.

3.65 When the contract provides liquidated damages for delay, the allocation of risk is that the Contractor is not liable for liquidated damages when the delay is caused by a Relevant Event even if concurrent. On that basis, there is no question of apportionment. The contractor is simply not liable. When damages for delay are unliquidated, then the general difficulty of proving loss when there is concurrency remains as described above. The extension of time provisions then have less relevance in determining the risk regime for the Employer's loss due to delay, since the extension of time provisions no longer determine the level of damages even indirectly. The general principle will then apply as described below in the context of contractor's claims for prolongation costs.

3.66 Mr Justice Dyson in *Henry Boot Construction (UK) Limited v Malmaison Hotel (Manchester) Ltd* [1999] rephrased the principle of Colman J in *Balfour Beatty Building Ltd v Chestermount Properties Ltd* [1993] 62 BLR 1.

3.66.1   He stated that the purpose of the power to grant an extension of time was to fix the period of time by which the time available for completion ought to be extended having regard to the incidence of the Relevant Events, measured by the standard of what is fair and reasonable.

3.66.2   He stated, although common ground, that the Completion Date as adjusted was not the date by which the Contractor ought to have achieved Practical Completion, but the end of the total number of working days starting from the date of possession within which the contractor **ought fairly and reasonably to have completed the works**.

3.67   In Example 1 in Figure 1 above, based on the above authorities and the principle stated by Colman J, the contractor is entitled to an extension of time in the case of concurrency even though one event under the terms of the contract is at his risk. The fairness in the approach is that the extension of time operates to relieve the contractor of liability for liquidated damages for events that are not at his risk. That is the system of risk allocation agreed by the Parties under the contract by the mechanism of extension of time and Relevant Events. It would be unfair to allow the employer to recover liquidated damages in a situation where the employer made a material contribution to the delay. In concurrency, the material contribution is co-extensive with the damages. Where the Relevant Event does not affect the completion date there is no material contribution to the damages and the issue of causation in law and the application of the contract risk regime does not arise. When liquidated damages are not part of the regime then the allocation of damages is applied on general principles including apportionment where appropriate.

3.68   The principle is not limited to the JCT form of contract, although it is necessary always to consider the actual contract regime of apportionment of risk. The principle was confirmed in *Motherwell Bridge Construction Ltd v Micafil AG* [2002]81ConLR44.

3.68.1   Micafil awarded Motherwell two subcontracts on FIDIC Yellow Book terms. HH Judge Toulmin QC referred to and adopted the approach of Dyson J in *Henry Boot Construction (UK) Ltd v Malmaison Hotel (Manchester) Ltd* [1999] even though the case was under the JCT Form. Clause 26.1 of the FIDIC Form provided that there was an entitlement to extension of time if Motherwell was or would be delayed in completing the works by any of the listed causes.

3.68.2   Toulmin J stated that if the delay was on the critical path and it had not been caused by Motherwell then he was required to assess how many additional days were to be awarded. If the delay was caused by the default of Motherwell then they were not entitled to any extension of time. He stated an example of the additional time required to carry out remedial works. He identified that the remedial works arose from Motherwell's failure to carry out the works in accordance with the contract.

3.68.3   Motherwell's claim was presented as two separate but related analyses.

3.68.4   The first analysis was to demonstrate that Motherwell's entitlement to extension of time due to the increased scope of work was a date beyond the date at which liability for liquidated damages would arise.

3.68.5   Motherwell used a theoretical impact as-planned programme analysis based on resources. The analysis demonstrated that Motherwell could not complete the increased works without employing additional resources beyond those envisaged at tender stage.

3.68.6   By taking into account the additional manhours required Motherwell calculated the date by which it was entitled to complete the works as varied. Motherwell argued that the resulting date from the analysis was the date by which Motherwell **ought fairly and reasonably** to have completed the works. Since the date was later than the date actually achieved, Motherwell argued that it could not be liable for liquidated damages.

3.68.7   The second analysis was based on the premise that prolonging the contract through no fault of Motherwell involved it in additional costs, including acceleration costs, which it was entitled to recover from Micafil.

3.68.8   Motherwell therefore adopted two different analyses for the two types of damage namely the employer's claim for delay damages and the contractor's claim for delay damage of additional prolongation costs.

3.68.9   Toulmin J accepted Motherwell's approach both in relation to extension of time under the contract and in relation to additional costs which Motherwell was entitled to claim for prolongation costs. He made it clear that the approach was subject to common sense and fairness.

3.69   The analysis is shown diagrammatically below in a simplistic form in Figure 5.

Figure 5 – Theoretical Impacted As-Planned Programme

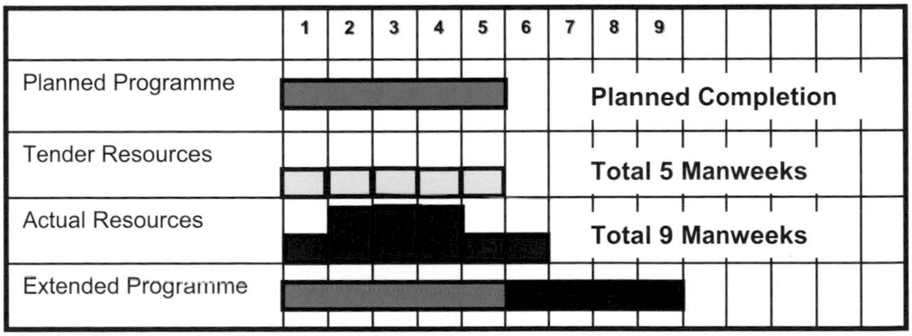

	1	2	3	4	5	6	7	8	9				
Planned Programme							**Planned Completion**						
Tender Resources							**Total 5 Manweeks**						
Actual Resources							**Total 9 Manweeks**						
Extended Programme													

Value Judgment of Allocation of Risk – Contractor's Claim for Damages for Delay

3.70   The above cases are concerned with the issue of delay in the particular situation of the contractor's obligation to complete by a specified date and the employer's right to liquidated damages. The general principle will usually apply when the contractor is claiming additional costs due to the delay. A different allocation of liability for delay may result due to the different damage claimed as recognised by Judge Fox-Andrews in *H Fairweather & Co Ltd v London Borough of Wandsworth* [1987]39BLR106 (QBD).

3.71   In the situation where liquidated damages are the issue, the allocation of liability for the employer's loss is indirectly through the determination of extension of time. Where the damage claimed is the contractor's prolongation costs then the mechanism of extension of time is not relevant, albeit that the same facts may apply.

3.72   In the Scots construction case of *John Doyle Construction Limited v Laing Management (Scotland) Limited* [2004] 1BLR 295 the Inner House considered the situation of separate events causing the same damage, namely delay in completion, and the contractor incurring and claiming additional time related costs. The delay would have occurred if one event had occurred without the other.

    3.72.1   It was held, in the case of concurrent causes if there is no dominant cause and the event which is the employer's responsibility in law is a material cause of the loss, that it may be possible to apportion the loss between the events. Apportionment is an application of the principled approach.

    3.72.2   Again, it was recognised that there is the requirement to satisfy the initial condition; otherwise, the issue of causation does not arise.

    3.72.3   The causes must be truly concurrent in the sense that they operate to produce a single consequence namely the same delay. The Inner House considered that it would be necessary to identify the periods when the causative events operated to cause the loss so as to determine their relative significance.

    3.72.4   It was considered that where the effects operated at the same time then there should be apportionment. This therefore is an example of an indivisible loss similar to the consequence in the medical negligence case of *Barker v St Gobain Pipelines plc* [2006]UKHL20 in which the House of Lords allowed apportionment of damages, subject to the availability of a sensible basis for apportionment.

    3.72.5   The Inner House illustrated the principle by an example where the work on a construction project might be held up for a period owing to the late provision of information by the architect, but during that period bad weather might have prevented work for part of the time.

    3.72.6   In such a case, it was considered that responsibility for the loss could be apportioned between the two causes, according to their relative significance.

Where the consequence was delay as against disruption, that could be done fairly readily on the basis of the time during which each of the causes was operative.

3.72.7 During the period when both operated, it was considered that each should normally be treated as contributing to the loss, with the result that the employer was responsible for only part of the delay during that period.

3.73 The analysis suggested by the Inner House in their example is shown diagrammatically below in Figure 6.

Figure 6 - Concurrent Events – Contractors Delay Damages

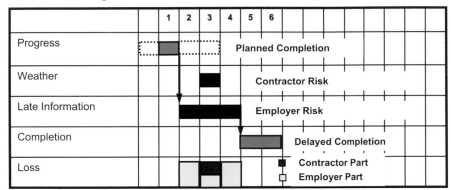

3.74 The approach of the Inner House was not based on a factual causation concept but on the basis of fair allocation of liability for prolongation costs.

3.75 The Inner House suggested in its example that the contractor would recover all his loss for the whole period of delay caused by the late information except for half his loss during the period when there was also concurrent adverse weather. It appears that the distinction being made by the Inner House is between neutral events such as weather and physical conditions and events that arise from actions or inactions of the contractor for which he could be considered culpable. For the latter events, it is appropriate to use the term "default" used by the Inner House (below). The legal basis for the distinction is not clear, but the judgment needs to be viewed in the context that the Inner Court was considering a global claim by the contractor and the difficulties of proof. If the employer is to be liable when he is clearly culpable, then it is fair that he should have no liability where the contractor is also culpable.

3.76 The Inner House clearly considered that it would be unjust to hold out from the contractor all additional costs which had been partly caused by events the responsibility of the employer, in a similar approach to the House of Lords in *Barker v St Gobain Pipelines plc* [2006]UKHL20. If the employer had plainly contributed to delay then it was appropriate that he should bear part of the damage.

3.77 The Inner House emphasised that any apportionment had to be based on the evidence and carried out on a basis that was reasonable in all the circumstances. It held that apportionment was also available in cases of disruption as well as delay and that the practical difficulties of analysis should not prevent a remedy.

3.78   The reduction in additional costs due to the contractor by apportionment is fair only if the effect of weather in the example is considered to be a neutral event outside the control of both parties, but not if the risk has been allocated to the contractor under the contract. The Inner House distinguished the above situation where the event was not the responsibility of the employer or the contractor, from one where the event was the contractor's responsibility.

3.79   The Inner Court suggests that the contractor will be denied recovery where a cause is his "responsibility" and use the term "default". Those terms suggest that actions or omissions by the contractor have operated to bring about the concurrent cause and so deny recovery. That language is not appropriate to describe a neutral event such as weather. Nonetheless, the risk regime of the contract may apportion risk of neutral events between the employer and the contractor. The allocation may distinguish risk allocation on the basis of the nature of the event such as "adverse inclement weather" or "unforeseen ground conditions".

3.80   If the contract provides a seamless risk regime, then the risk of additional costs for all events will be allocated to either the employer or the contractor. There is no reason in that case why apportionment should apply. All concurrent events will be the responsibility of one of the parties or events will be divided between them depending on their nature. If there are two concurrent events, one the responsibility of the contractor and the other the responsibility of the employer, then fairness would suggest that the employer should not be liable for all of the costs in the period of concurrent delay.

3.81   The approach by the Inner Court is a logical extension of the Colman J principle, but the timing of the incidence of the Contractor's risk event needs to be considered. In the case of weather in the example, which is time dependant, the allocation of liability may be different if the weather occurs in the original contract period or if it occurs in an extended period caused by the employer's late information. For this situation by analogy, see Example 2 below.

3.82   Apportionment only applies where neither concurrent event can be considered a dominant cause. The dominant cause theory is to be distinguished from the situation where one event caused by one of the parties influences the actions of the other party. So for instance if the contractor is aware that the works are to be delayed due to matters the responsibility of or at the risk of the Employer, he may delay the delivery of certain materials or the commencement of part of the works as part of efficient planning of the works. A retrospective analysis may show superficially concurrent causes of delay, whereas one event has in fact set the circumstances for the second event.

3.83   If an event occurs which prevents another event from operating at all, then the intervening event as a matter of logic is the sole cause of the consequence. That is a different situation to one where a separate event takes place in the context of another event that continues to act.

3.6 THE GENERAL PRINCIPLES OF CAUSATION IN CONSTRUCTION LAW

3.84   Based on the above decided cases the Principled Approach for establishing causation in construction law is in summary as follows.

    3.84.1   The initial condition for causation needs to be satisfied. If the event could not have affected the damage related to the particular obligation in issue, then the matter of causation does not arise. So, if the particular obligation that the Contractor shall complete by a date and the event could not have affected completion then causation does not arise.

    3.84.2   Evidence must be adduced to allow the inference to be made that the event occurred and that it was a breach of a legal obligation which entitles compensation for the damage.

    3.84.3   If the indivisible damage is caused by one party to the contract and third parties, then the party in default is the cause in law as between the Parties for the whole of the damage on the basis of joint and several liability. If that party wishes, he may seek contribution from the third parties.

    3.84.4   If it is possible to identify one event from many as the dominant or effective cause of the indivisible damage, then that event is the sole cause in law of the damage.

    3.84.5   A value judgment is required of the particular obligation in issue and whether or not it is fair that the party in breach of the obligation should make at least some contribution for the indivisible damage and where appropriate in proportion to the material contribution to the change in risk caused by the parties.

    3.84.6   The allocation of risk under the contract must be given effect by preventing any allocation of liability which would upset that risk allocation. If the contract is silent on the allocation of risk then there should be apportionment of loss for concurrent events provided both events are a material cause and neither can be considered a dominant cause. In the context of liquidated damages and the contractor's obligation to complete the works, in the case of concurrency the issue of apportionment does not arise. In that situation, it is unfair to the contractor to fix a completion date which would make the contractor liable in liquidated damages for events which were not the contractor's risk.

    3.84.7   The resulting allocation of responsibility must be consistent with common sense.

3.7. INDIVISIBLE DAMAGE – APPLICATION OF GENERAL PRINCIPLE

3.85   The general principle is applied below for the examples 2 and 3 already examined in the "but-for" test and the New Intervening Event concept.

Example 2 – Events During Culpable Delay

3.86   Example 2 is the situation where a risk event occurs in a period of culpable delay caused by the contractor described by Colman J A in *Balfour Beatty Building Ltd v Chestermount Properties Ltd* [1993]62BLR1 *QBD*. The contract was substantially in the JCT Standard Form 1980, Private Edition with Approximate Quantities. The judgment turned on the interpretation of the contract in the context of the application of liquidated damages.

3.87   Example 2 is shown diagrammatically below in Figure 7 showing the period of culpable delay and the additional delay caused by the risk event. Three different scenarios are examined below previously examined in relation to the "but-for" test and the New Intervening Event.

Figure 7 - Separate Causes – Employers Delay Damages

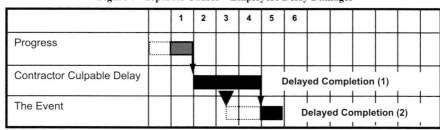

3.88   <u>Example 2.1</u> is the situation where the event is the flooding of the site due to a storm, which occurs after the contract completion date in a period of contractor culpable delay. The storm causes flooding of the site, which results in further delay. As described above in this situation the "but for" test leads to the conclusion that the event causing the culpable delay also caused the damage; the storm and the consequent flooding would not have had a further effect on progress if the contractor had completed by the contract completion date. As also described above the New Intervening Event concept does not provide a solution since the storm and the resulting flooding are not so unusual or out of the ordinary.

3.89   The Principled Approach leads to the conclusion that in the context of the application of liquidated damages, the storm and resulting flooding were caused in law by the contractor.

3.89.1   The event of the flooding as a result of a storm affected actual completion so that the initial condition is satisfied.

3.89.2   The allocation of risk under the Contract is that the Employer carries the risk of flooding due to storms. Unless there are clear words to the contrary this allocation of risk and the regime of liquidated damages will apply during the whole period of construction, the contract period and the extended contract period. It will also apply in the period of culpable delay after the Contract completion date or extended date, provided the risk has not been materially increased by the contractor.

3.89.3   The contractor's obligation in this case is to complete by the contract completion date. Unless there are clear words to the contrary, the Employer does not assume responsibility for risk events arising solely because of the contractor's default of that obligation, in this case in the period of his culpable delay.

3.89.4   Since the storm and the flooding are time dependant, the period of culpable delay caused by the contractor has materially increased the risk of a storm and the resulting flooding. The contractor therefore carries the risk of storms and consequent flooding in the period of culpable delay.

3.89.5   It is not unfair to the contractor that he should be denied an extension of time for the flooding due to a storm; it does not upset the contract allocation of risk but to the contrary, gives effect to it. It is not unfair to the contractor that he should be liable for liquidated damages for the whole period of culpable delay and the extended period caused by the flooding due to a storm.

3.89.6   Apportionment of loss does not arise since the Employer has not made any material contribution to the delay. In any event, the regime of liquidated damages would prevent the operation of that principle – the liquidated damages apply or they do not.

3.89.7   The resulting allocation of responsibility is consistent with common sense.

3.90   The result of the principled approach is shown diagrammatically below in Figure 8.

Figure 8 – Example 2.1 - The Storm in a Period of Culpable Delay

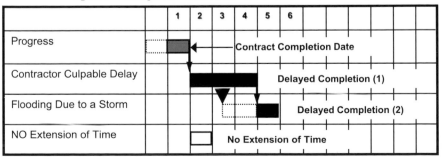

3.91   Colman J in *Balfour Beatty Building Ltd v Chestermount Properties Ltd* [1993]62BLR1 *QBD* considered and rejected the argument by Balfour Beatty that there was a temporal limit on all categories of Relevant Events, so that the extension of time and liquidated damages regime only operated for Relevant Events which occurred before the contract completion date.   The basis for rejecting this interpretation of the contract was that it was contrary to the scheme of risk distribution under the contract.

3.92   Colman J therefore made a distinction between events that are time-dependant and those that are dependant on progress.   Under the JCT Forms, a local authority or statutory utility interruption of work would be treated as a Relevant Event if the interruption had occurred before the completion date.   In the case where the event the event was caused by the state of progress of the works and not because of the period of culpable delay itself, Colman J considered that the general scheme of risk distribution under the contract applied even after the contract completion date.

3.93   When considering a time-dependant event, the approach of Colman J was to consider whether that event could have been avoided if the contractor had not been in culpable delay.   He referred to the example a storm that flooded the site during a period of culpable delay and interrupted progress of the works.   He observed that the flooding would have been avoided altogether if the contractor had not overrun the completion date.

3.94   Colman J considered that it would not be fair and reasonable to grant an extension of time unless the contractor was able to show that even if he had not been in culpable delay the event would have still delayed completion at an earlier date.   He considered that such cases were not likely to be a common occurrence.

3.95   The reasoning of Colman J is consistent with the "but – for" test, but is a principled approach based on the concepts of fairness and reasonableness.   The particular contract risk regime places the risk of flooding caused by storms on the employer.   Although it can be said that the default of the contractor does not directly cause the storm which is an independent event caused by weather, nonetheless, the incidence of the storm cannot be considered to be a mere coincidence in the context of the contractor's default.   The default by the contractor of his obligation as to time increases the period of construction, increases the risk of flooding due to a storm and the chances of avoiding it are lessened. In that sense the default by the contractor was a cause of the risk event.   The allocation of the risk regime for the whole of the construction period is not applied mechanically, but recognises the material increase in risk of an event due to the contractor's breach of contract.

3.96   The reasoning is consistent with common sense.   There is no reason why the employer should not be compensated by liquidated damages for the full period of culpable delay and the further delay due to flooding, unless it can be shown that the delay due to the storm would have occurred in any event.   The incidence of the storm is time dependant and was caused in the widest sense by the contractor's culpable delay.

3.97   Example 2.2 is the situation where the prolonged period is within the contract period. The contractor has been delayed on planned programme on part of the works for matters for which he is responsible. That part is not on the critical path to completion at that time so that the contractor is still on course to complete by the contract completion date. The storm occurs during the contract period. If the part had not been delayed, it would have reached a stage of construction that would have prevented the flooding of the site by the storm. The delay caused by the flooding is greater than the "float" on that part and changes the critical path resulting in delay to completion.

3.98   The Principled Approach leads to the conclusion that in the context of the application of liquidated damages, the storm and resulting flooding were not caused in law by the contractor.

3.98.1   The event of the flooding as a result of a storm affected actual completion so that the initial condition is satisfied.

3.98.2   The allocation of risk under the Contract is that the Employer carries the risk of flooding due to storms during the whole period of construction, the contract period and the extended contract period.

3.98.3   The contractor's obligation in this case is to complete by the contract completion date. The contractor is not in default of that obligation. Unless there is an obligation to follow the planned programme, the contractor is not in default of his contractual obligations. The delay on the planned programme is not a default but simply part of the flexibility required on a Contract to manage the works.

3.98.4   The action or inaction of the contractor has not materially increased the risk of a storm and the resulting flooding. The storm and the flooding are precisely the risk anticipated by the contract in the contract period. The Employer therefore carries the risk of storms and consequent flooding.

3.98.5   It is not unfair to the Employer that the contractor is granted an extension of time for the flooding due to a storm; it does not upset the contract allocation of risk but to the contrary, gives effect to it.

3.98.6   Apportionment of loss does not arise since the contractor has not made any material contribution to the delay; the delay in the planned part of the work did not delay completion that was caused solely by the storm and flooding. In any event, the regime of liquidated damages would prevent the operation of that principle – the liquidated damages apply or they do not.

3.98.7   The resulting allocation of responsibility is consistent with common sense.

3.99   The result of the principled approach is shown diagrammatically below in Figure 9.

Figure 9 – Example 2.2 - The Storm in a Period of Delay in the Contract Period

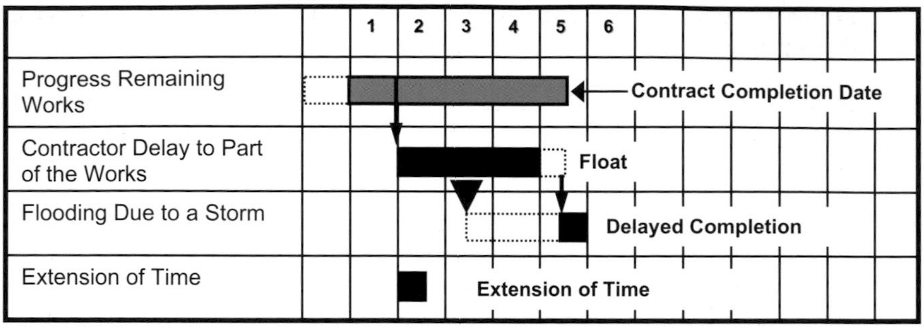

3.100   The delay to progress of the part of the works is simply a coincidence creating the circumstances in which the damage from the risk event of the storm took place. The action or inaction of the contractor does not increase the risk of a storm and the flooding during the contract period. The flooding due to a storm in this case is an event the responsibility of the employer under the risk regime, the very type of risk envisaged. It is simply a coincidence that the storm occurred at a stage of construction during the contract period that resulted in flooding.

3.101   Example 2.3 is the situation where the event is an instructed variation to the contract issued after the contract completion date in a period of contractor culpable delay. That was the substantive issue in *Balfour Beatty Building Ltd v Chestermount Properties Ltd* [1993]62BLR1 QBD. The contract was substantially in the JCT Standard Form 1980, Private Edition with Approximate Quantities. The contractor Balfour Beatty contracted with Chestermount for the construction of the shell and core of an office block. By January 1990, the works were not expected to be completed until July 1990. Between 12 February and 12 July 1990, the architect issued instructions for fit-out works as variations to the contract. Throughout this period, the shell and core works remained incomplete.

3.102   Unlike the storm, a variation cannot be assumed to be time dependant. It cannot be inferred that the period of culpable delay is directly linked to the incidence of the event. A sub-analysis is required, to establish which of three possible sub-scenarios applies.

3.102.1 The culpable delay dictated the need and timing of the instructed variation.

3.102.2 The progress of the works identified the need for a variation and determined the timing.

3.102.3 The event was an entirely separate event independent of the progress of the works or the culpable delay.

60

3.103   In the first sub-scenario, the variation may arise only because of the circumstances created by the culpable delay the default of the contractor. An example would be a change in design due to out of sequence working resulting from the delay. A further example would be a change in construction materials due to the effects of time dependant events on the construction such as low temperatures.

3.104   In that case the "but for" test leads to the conclusion that the additional delay was caused by the event causing the culpable delay. The New Independent Event concept does not provide a solution.

3.105   In this first sub-scenario, the Principled Approach analysis in Example 2.1 above could be said to apply since the incidence of the variation and the storm are both he result of the contractor's default. There is of course one important difference between the storm and the variation. The variation is an act of the Employer. It is the nature of that act which determines whether or not the analysis in Example 2.1 applies.

3.106   If the contractor is not entitled to an extension of time for the further delay in carrying out the varied work, this would appear to be indistinguishable from a variation that is an act of prevention because of the absence of an appropriate extension of time provision.

3.107   If the issue of the variation instruction is necessary to allow the work to be completed at all, then it is not the voluntary conduct of the Employer. If the variation instruction reduces the overall delay that would have occurred, then the issue of the variation instruction is a voluntary act but is a measure of mitigation to reduce the consequences of the contractor's default. In that situation the apparent further delay resulting from the variation is simply a continuation and consequence of the culpable delay. In short, the Relevant Event of the instructed variation did not cause further or any delay at all but reduced the consequences of the contractor's default. On a proper analysis, the initial condition is not satisfied since the Relevant Event has not in fact caused delay and no extension of time need be considered. The variation will be valued in accordance with the provisions of the contract, but the Employer will be entitled to recover liquidated damages for both the period of culpable delay and the period of apparent further delay resulting from the necessary variation.

3.108   The above conclusion shows the importance of a proper analysis of the events and the effect of the variation on actual progress and whether the variation is involuntary and/or a mitigation measure as opposed to an independent voluntary act. The requirement to satisfy the necessary initial condition does not affect the agreed allocation of risk, even though the varied work is carried out at the same time as the original, albeit delayed, work.

3.109   Other than in the above restricted situation, the analysis in Example 2.1 will not apply in the case of variations causing further delay, since the variation will be a voluntary act of the Employer. Instead, the analysis below will then apply.

3.110   If the instructed variation is dictated by the progress of the works and only became apparent at that stage of construction, then it follows that it would have been issued in any event even if the culpable delay had not occurred.   That sub-scenario is analytically no different to the third sub-scenario where the instructed variation is entirely independent of the contractor's default.

3.111   The "but for" test leads to the conclusion that the additional delay would have occurred even without the period of culpable delay and therefore not caused by the event causing the culpable delay. The New Independent Event concept does not provide a solution.

3.112   In both the second and third sub-scenarios, the Principled Approach leads to the conclusion that in the context of the application of liquidated damages, the instructed variation entitles the contractor to an extension of time and relief from liquidated damages for the period of further delay as a result of the variation.

   3.112.1   The instructed variation affected actual completion so that the initial condition is satisfied.

   3.112.2   Instructed variations under the Contract entitle the contractor to extension of time which subject to terms to the contrary, applies both during the contract period and the period of culpable delay.   If that is not the case then the variation will be an act of prevention with the possibility that the regime of liquidated damages will no longer apply in any event.

   3.112.3   The contractor's obligation is to carry out instructed variations and the risk of delay caused by the variation lies with the Employer through the mechanism of the Relevant Event.

   3.112.4   It is not unfair to the Employer that he should be denied liquidated damages for the period of delay caused by the instructed variation.   The issue of the instructed variation is a voluntary act; the above allocation of responsibility does not upset the contract allocation of risk but to the contrary, gives effect to it.

   3.112.5   Apportionment of loss does not arise since the contractor has not made any material contribution to the delay.   In any event, the regime of liquidated damages would prevent the operation of that principle – the liquidated damages apply or they do not.

   3.112.6   The resulting allocation of responsibility is consistent with common sense.

3.113   The result of the principled approach is shown diagrammatically below in Figure 10.

Figure 10 – Example 2.3 – Instructed Variation in a Period of Culpable Delay

		1	2	3	4	5	6						
Progress				Contract Completion Date									
Contractor Culpable Delay						Delayed Completion (1)							
Instructed Variation							Delayed Completion (2)						
Extension of Time				Extension of Time									

Example 3 – Events During Extended Period of Contract

3.114   Example 3 is the situation of a risk event of a strike occurring in an extended period of the contract. The example was described in *H Fairweather & Co Ltd v London Borough of Wandsworth* [1987]39BLR106 (QBD).

3.115   The essential facts of the example are that an instructed variation had led to an extension of the contract period by 3 months. Two weeks before the end of the extended period a strike prevents further work being carried out over winter, a period of 5 months. The effect of the delay into winter is that essential maintenance on tunnelling equipment could not be carried out. In practice, it is not clear how the winter season would prevent maintenance, nor how any maintenance could be carried out in any event with the strike in place. Nonetheless, those are the assumed facts. As a result, on restart 6 weeks maintenance work is required before the remaining two weeks work can be commenced.

3.116   The above facts are shown diagrammatically in Figure 11 below.

Figure 11 – Example 3 – Relevant Event in an Extended Period

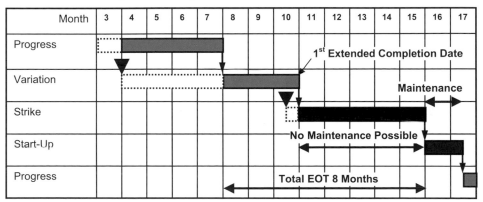

3.117   As described above, the "but for" test leads to the conclusion that the instructed variation caused all the consequences in both time and cost including the consequences of the seasonal effects on maintenance. The test is not sufficient since it takes no account of the allocation of risk under the contract.

3.118   In addition, as described above, in the situation where the contract makes provision for the incidence of strikes, the concept of New Intervening Event does not lead to a sole cause but leaves open the cause of further delay between the event causing the contractor's delay and the strike.

3.119   The starting point for the Principled Approach is the allocation of risk under the contract. In this case the contract is the JCT Local Authorities Edition with Quantities 1963 Edition (July 1973 Revision). It is a feature of JCT Forms that there are two risk regimes, one for loss and expense under Clause 11 and the other for liquidated damages through the extension of time provisions in Clause 23. Clause 11 provides a list of matters which entitle the contractor to loss and expense incurred provided other conditions are met. Clause 11 does not include "strikes" as one of the matters. Clause 23 lists "strikes" as a Relevant Event entitling the contractor to an extension of time. Neither clause lists unexceptional weather as founding a contractor's entitlement.

3.120   The scheme of risk apportionment is that loss and expense resulting from delay caused by strikes falls on both employer and contractor. The employer will lose his right to liquidated damages in respect of any extension of time given by the architect under Clause 23. Since loss and expense suffered by the contractor resulting from strikes is not a matter within Clause 24 or the default of the Employer, the contractor bears his own loss and expense. In this regard Judge Fox-Andrews applied *Henry Boot Construction Limited v Central Lancashire New Town Development Corporation* [1980] 15 BLR 1.

3.121   Judge Fox-Andrews considered that if the architect granted an extension of time of eight months only under Clause 23 there was no reason why the contractor under the contract could not still recover all his direct loss and expense under Clause 11. He considered that an extension of time under Clause 23 was neither expressly nor impliedly a condition precedent to a right to payment under Clause 11. His analysis of the theoretical situation stopped at this point, since it was only intended to demonstrate that the analysis of causation depends on the damage claimed.

3.122   The main issue in Example 3 in determining whether the Employer is entitled to deduct liquidated damages and whether the Contractor is entitled to loss and expense, is whether the contract allocation of risk applies unaltered to the whole period of construction.

3.123   The Principled Approach leads to the conclusion that in the context of the application of liquidated damages, that the Contractor is entitled to an additional extension of time of 3 months as a result of the strike as well as a further extension of 6 weeks for the delay due to maintenance at the end of that period. The Contractor is therefore entitled to relief from liquidated damages for the whole period of delay[19].

---

[19]   The assumption is that the strike is the type of strike identified as a Relevant Event under the contract. Whether or not this is the case will depend upon the interpretation of the contract see for example *Henry Boot Construction Ltd v Central Lancashire New Town Development Corporation* [1980]15 BLR 8 and *Boskalis Westminster Construction Ltd - v Liverpool City Council* [1993] 24 BLR 87.

3.123.1 The strike and the seasonal effect on maintenance affected actual completion so that the initial condition is satisfied.

3.123.2 The Contractor is entitled to an extension of time for the variation during the original contract period. The extension of time not only relieves the Contractor from liability for liquidated damages but also provides him with the same protection and benefits as under in the original contract period by analogy with the reasoning of Colman J in *Balfour Beatty Building Ltd v Chestermount Properties Ltd* [1993]62BLR1 QBD. The Contractor is entitled to further extensions of time for additional variations in the extended period and even in a period of culpable delay provided they cause further delay. If it was otherwise, any variation in the first extended period would be an act of prevention and the liquidated damage regime would fall. The Contractor not only has the revised obligation but the entitlement to complete by the extended contract completion date. Accordingly, subject to express terms to the contrary, the same allocation of risk in relation to liquidated damages applies during the extended contract period as applied during the original period.

3.123.3 When the strike occurs, the contractor is not in default of his obligation to complete by the extended date. The contractor has not materially increased the risk of a strike which is precisely the risk anticipated under the contract. Accordingly, the Employer carries the time risk of the strike and the Contractor is entitled to a second extension of time of 5 months, the duration of the strike.

3.123.4 By the same reasoning as above, the same allocation of risk as applies in the original contract period applies in the second extended period of 5 months. Accordingly, it may be argued that the 6 week delay was caused by the seasonal effect and the risk of weather lies with the Contractor under the contract.

3.123.5 That however ignores the dominant effect of the strike. When the strike occurs, the Contractor has 2 weeks work left to complete and is on time. The seasonal effect on maintenance would not have prevented the Contractor completing. The effect of the strike is subsequently to prevent the Contractor carrying out maintenance of the tunnelling equipment, by extending the construction period into the winter. The seasonal effect is not simply a coincidence, or part of the risk regime but is a consequence of the strike and cannot be separated from it. It is the strike which is the dominant cause of the delay and there is no concurrency of events. Accordingly, the Contractor is entitled to the further extension of 6 weeks.

3.123.6 It is not unfair to the Employer that he should be denied liquidated damages for the period of delay caused by the strike and the 6 week period at start up. The issue of the variation in the original contract period is a voluntary act and created the possibility of events such as strikes and the consequential seasonal effects. The grant of an extension of time for the strike and the start up period does not upset the contract allocation of risk but to the contrary, gives effect to it.

3.123.7　The resulting allocation of responsibility is consistent with common sense, since it maintains the risk regime agreed by the parties under the contract.

3.124　The Principled Approach leads to the conclusion that the Contractor is entitled to loss and expense for the 5 month and the 6 week period.

3.124.1　The strike and the seasonal effect on maintenance affected the contractor's costs so that the initial condition is satisfied.

3.124.2　The risk regime under the contract is that the Contractor is not entitled to loss and expense for the incidence of strikes. Although the first extended period was caused by an instructed variation, the starting point is that the contract risk regime for loss and expense is the same in the extended period as in the original period in the absence of clear words to the contrary. It follows that if the risk regime is applied unaltered that the Contractor is not entitled to loss and expense incurred either during the 5 month period or the 6 week period. The issue is whether under the contract the Contractor has assumed the risks of loss and expense for events in the first extended period.

3.124.3　The strike is not in the ordinary course of things time dependant and is independent of the first extended period[20]. Although the strike does not flow directly from the Variation, it does not necessarily follow that the Contractor has assumed the risk of the loss and expense resulting from the strike. The Contractor is allocated the risk of loss and expense for the effect of strikes in the original contract period and will be taken to have included for that risk in his prices. The Contractor will be entitled to additional payment for the Variation. Unless the mechanism for valuation of the Variation makes express provision in the valuation for pricing the risks during the first extended period, then the Contractor does not assume responsibility for risk events occurring in the first extended period. In that case, the contract risk regime should not be applied unaltered in the extended period. Instead, the Contractor is entitled to his costs flowing from the strike for the second extended period.

3.124.4　As described above, the strike is the dominant cause of the winter and therefore the lack of maintenance. Accordingly, the loss and expense in the six week period is a natural consequence of the strike. The Contractor is entitled to the loss and expense incurred in the six week period.

3.124.5　It is not unfair to the Employer that he should reimburse the Contractor for the indirect consequences of the Variation which created the possibility of events such as strikes and the consequential seasonal effects. The reimbursement is either through the price for the risk in the valuation of the Variation or if there is no such mechanism the reimbursement of the

---

[20]　It is assumed that the strike is not related solely to the site nor the Contractor but takes place in a wider political context.

Contractor's loss and expense. In either event, effect is given to the contract allocation of risk.

3.124.6 The resulting allocation of responsibility is consistent with common sense, since the Employer is required either to reimburse the cost of the Variation including an amount for the assumed risk, or reimburses the Contractor for a risk which he has not assumed. This maintains the risk regime agreed by the parties under the contract.

3.8. INDIVISIBLE DAMAGE - COMPOUND CAUSATION

3.125 The medical negligence cases described above show the approach of the courts when there are difficulties of proof in identifying which of a number of possible events may have caused indivisible damage. A different issue arises when the default of the plaintiff and the defendant are insufficient to cause the defect in the absence of the other. This is an example of "composite" or "compound" causation.

3.126 In *W Lamb Ltd v J Jarvis & Sons plc* [1998] ORB the plaintiff subcontractor installed pipework to a petrol filling station for the contractor defendant.

3.126.1 The pipework leaked and was replaced. The matter to be decided as a preliminary issue was whether the failure was caused by the faulty workmanship on the pipework by the plaintiff or acts or omissions in the construction of the concrete supports by the defendant.

3.126.2 It was found that failure was caused equally by the plaintiff and the defendant. The defaults were each insufficient to cause the leaks in the absence of the other.

3.126.3 It was held that following *Tennant Radiant Heat Ltd v Warrington Development Corporation* [1988] 1 EGLR 41 that the court was entitled to ascertain and exercise the jurisdiction to apportion where required to do justice.

3.127 The approach is an example of the Principled Approach where each of the Parties has made material contributions to the indivisible damage.

3.9. SINGLE SOLUTION – SEPARATE CAUSES

3.128 A further situation arises when the separate defaults of the employer and contractor result in a single remedial solution and again the approach has been to apportion liability.

3.129 In *Musselburgh and Fisherrow Cooperative Society Limited v Mowlem Scotland Limited (No 2)* [2006]CSOH39 Mowlem constructed a leisure centre for Musselburgh under a design and build contract.

3.129.1 The action concerned certain defects in a swimming pool forming part of a leisure centre. There were three defects. The first defect was the responsibility of Mowlem and was defective rendering in the swimming pool which caused seepage. The second defect was the responsibility of Musselburgh and was a design defect in which the waterproof membrane did not extend under the deck level channel and over the floor slab of the adjacent walkway. The third defect was also the responsibility of Musselburgh and related to the detail of the pipework draining the overflow water in the channel.

3.129.2   The solution on advice of experts was to provide a completely new waterproof membrane because it was undesirable to join new and existing membranes of different age and material.

3.129.3   Mowlem argued that the claim for replacement of the membrane was a global claim. Since Musselburgh had not eliminated from the causes of loss all matters not the responsibility of Mowlem, it was argued that the claim failed on the basis of the principles in *John Doyle Construction Limited v Laing Management (Scotland) Limited* [2004] 1BLR 295 Inner House.

3.129.4   Musselburgh on the other hand argued that there was a single loss, namely the need to replace the waterproof membrane, and since Mowlem's default was a material contribution it was liable for all of the loss relying on *Monarch Steamship Co Ltd v Karlshamns Oljefabriker* [1949]HL AC196 and *The Royal Brompton Hospital NHS Trust v Watkins Gray International* [2000] QBD (TCC) ConLR148.

3.129.5   Lord Eassie held that Musselburgh could not recover the whole of the cost from Mowlem, because the seepage due to the defective rendering was not the dominant cause of the global expense of the replacement membrane. Indeed, he found that between the three causes there was no dominant cause. On that basis, Lord Eassie proceeded to apportion the cost.

3.129.6   He apportioned the cost of lifting and replacing the channel and gutter three ways between the causes. The remaining costs he apportioned two ways between the defective render cause and the absent membrane to the gutter cause only since he considered that the defective pipework cause did not contribute to the remaining membrane replacement cost.

CHAPTER 4 – CAUSATION AND LOGIC

4.1 THE USE OF PROGRAMMES

4.1 Sometimes the link between the event and the delay can be made without any elaborate analysis. The measure of complexity of a situation is not dependant upon the complexity of the project, but on the event and its consequences. So for example, if the event prevents commencement of the project at all by denial of access, then the consequences of that event may not be difficult to assess. Although even in that situation the analysis may be complicated if the project could not commence for other reasons such as the inability to mobilise plant, the failure to obtain necessary regulatory permissions or the failure to progress design. There may also be issues of mitigation. Similarly if the event occurs towards the end of construction and delays the only remaining operation, such as attendance at a performance test, the analysis may not be overly complicated.

4.2 Often there will be a number of possible causes of delay against the background of complex arrangements of resources and operations, with an inter-dependence which is not always obvious. A programme analysis of the competing effects of those events may then assist in the analysis. Causation in law is not determined from an impressionistic view but rather must be a calculated assessment of the extension of time *John Barker Construction Ltd v London Portman Hotel Ltd* [1996] 83 BLR 31 and a critical path analysis is usually required *Balfour Beatty Construction Ltd v The Mayor and Burgess of LB Lambeth* [2002] EWHC 597 (TCC).

4.3 HH Judge Toulmin observed in *Mirant Asia-Pacific Construction (Hong Kong) Limited v Ove Arup and Partners International Limited* [2007]EWHC918(TCC) that the term "critical path" was defined by BS.6079 -2.2000 Part 2, 2.41 as the sequence of activities through a project network from start to finish, the sum of whose durations determined the overall project duration. He accepted that the critical path could not be identified inductively, by assertion. Although the point was not developed in his judgment, Toulmin J recognised and accepted that there may not only be more than one critical path, but that it is important to look at activities at or near the critical path to understand their potential impact on the project. Implicit in that observation is that any critical path analysis is uncertain since it is based on uncertain data. This aspect of delay analysis is examined in detail below. It is necessary to consider near critical activities not only because of the inherent uncertainty of any analysis, but because in practice the incidence of near critical activities may have influenced the behaviour of those involved in the project and the decisions made.

4.4 The delay analysis required is usually based on actual delay to actual progress of the works and not delay to the planned progress as shown on an approved or accepted programme, although this depends upon the terms of the contract and the nature of the damage. In that case, simply showing that the timing of the issue of drawings and instructions did not comply with the programme may not be sufficient to establish causation. In *Walter Lawrence and Sons Ltd v Commercial Union Properties (UK) Ltd* [1986] 4 ConLR 37 the provisions of clause 23(b) of JCT 63 relating to extensions of time for exceptionally inclement weather were examined. It was held that the effect was to be assessed at the time the work was actually carried out and not when they were programmed to be carried out.

4.5   In *Mirant Asia-Pacific Construction (Hong Kong) Limited v Ove Arup and Partners International Limited* [2007]EWHC918(TCC) Toulmin J observed that an analysis is valid only if it takes into account all activities and must include the time to the end of the project, otherwise events may occur after the period of analysis which take an activity onto the (or a) critical path. He considered that any analysis that did not do so was seriously flawed.

4.6   The modern approach in construction is to manage the project using both contracting arrangements and programmes. It might be assumed that such an approach would easily allow subsequent logical analysis of events to establish the causes of delay. That however underestimates the complexity of arrangements and the impact of unplanned events on such arrangements.

4.7   In *The Royal Brompton Hospital NHS Trust v Watkins Gray International* [2000] QBD (TCC) ConLR148 His Honour Judge Richard Seymour QC observed that the analysis of causation in building projects depended upon the relationship of the building operations and recognised the difficulty of establishing the construction logic.

4.8   Where the issue is the contractor's obligation to complete by a specified date, a programme will be needed to show that the particular event is on the critical path to completion. This point was emphasised by His Honour Judge Richard Seymour QC in *The Royal Brompton Hospital NHS Trust v Watkins Gray International* [2000] QBD (TCC) ConLR148.

4.8.1   Seymour J considered that in order to make an assessment of whether a particular occurrence had affected the ultimate completion of the work, rather than just a particular operation, it was desirable to consider what operations at the time the event happened were critical to the forward progress of the work as a whole.

4.8.2   Seymour J recognised that it was important to identify the construction logic and observed that the critical path may change during the course of the works particularly if progress is affected by an unplanned event.

4.8.3   He accepted the views of experts that different methods of assessment were likely to produce different results, perhaps dramatically different results.

4.8.4   He also accepted that the accuracy of any of the methods in common use critically depended upon the quality of the information upon which the assessment exercise was based.

4.9   It is remarkable that delay analysis by experts produce such different results. In many cases, this is not simply a difference of opinion of experts. Frequently the experts have different views on the facts and apply different construction logic as well as using different methods of analysis. It is necessary therefore to question the accuracy of every aspect of any model presented as a delay analysis, the activities, the timescale and the construction logic.

4.10   Although a sensible and pragmatic view particularly in the context of the realities of the construction site is usually adopted, mere common sense is not enough. Facts need to be proved and to be effective the proof must at least be adequate. The evidence of an expert, particularly with direct hands-on knowledge of the various project packages will be highly cogent if the expert is objective, meticulous as to detail and importantly not adhering inflexibly to theory when the proven facts are inconsistent with computer programme logic. The expert must have sufficient intellectual rigour to admit to the possibility of doubt in his analysis when faced with new evidence particularly from another expert[21].

4.11   The availability of evidence, the quality of the evidence and the nature of the issues dictates the appropriate method of analysis that can be adopted.

4.12   A programme used during construction to organise the work may properly show the intended plan but not the construction logic necessary to carry out an accurate delay analysis. Frequently that programme cannot be adopted for analysis without re-construction of the construction logic.

4.13   Construction projects are the product of human endeavour, albeit subject to natural forces. Each part of the project is therefore subject to a construction logic that defines necessary conditions for the work to commence, proceed and to be completed. The engineers and managers who have been involved with the project for some time invariably have a firm understanding of the main events and the construction logic, but frequently the experts appointed to analyse delay overlook their evidence. Unfortunately, the evidence submitted by experts does not always assist in clearly establishing causation.

4.14   The accuracy of the method of delay analysis depends upon the accuracy of the model of the following main dimensions of the project.

4.14.1   Activity work content.

4.14.2   Timing of the activity.

4.14.3   The effort in terms of labour, materials, plant and energy.

4.14.4   The construction logic.

4.15   Programme analysis invariably introduces technical language of its own, which does not always assist in the analysis and generally clouds the issues. The use of computer programme software itself introduces assumptions and inferences that need to be recognised and accommodated if the logic of any analysis is to be accurate. The mathematical model generated by commercially available software programmes to analyse events may contain hidden assumptions that make the analysis inaccurate.

---

[21]   HH Judge Wilcox in *Skanska Construction UK Ltd v Eggar (Barony) Ltd* [2004] EWHC 1748 .

The logic links between activities may not be sufficiently robust to accurately model the consequences of multiple events.

4.16 Although some commercially available computer programme software may have their limitations, they are still likely to be effective in delay analysis if they have a significant capacity for logical connections, for identifying critical paths and for re-scheduling activities to show events change. The fact that a particular programme was used to manage the project may be an advantage in delay analysis even with the limitations of the software[22].

4.17 Programmes have an important part to play in presenting the relevant facts in a time framework, in demonstrating the essential construction logic and in allowing factual analysis of causation, but their importance should not be overstated. As Toulmin J observed in *Mirant Asia-Pacific Construction (Hong Kong) Limited v Ove Arup and Partners International Limited* [2007]EWHC918(TCC) the use of programmes and particularly critical path analysis is only a tool which must be considered with other evidence. Delay was a question of fact and evidence of programme experts may be persuasive.

4.18 In *London Underground Limited v Citylink Telecommunications Ltd* [2007] EWHC 1749 (TCC) CTL's case on causation was based largely on inferences drawn from factual and expert evidence and various exercises to establish the necessary causation.

4.18.1 The Arbitrator rejected those approaches. In the Award, the Arbitrator concluded that in relation to delay, the Connect Project was not best suited to analysis by the Critical Path Method and there was therefore no satisfactory means of measuring delay by reference to critical path analysis.

4.18.2 Ramsey J deciding the application challenging the award held that the question of what was fair and reasonable in the circumstances, which was the yardstick under the contract for the assessment of extension of time, was not tied to a particular analysis nor was the arbitrator bound to follow the contentions of the parties. The assessment was one that necessarily had a subjective element and was based on an assessment of the circumstances.

4.18.3 Ramsey J held that whilst analysis of critical delay by one of a number of well-known methods was often relied on and could assist in arriving at a conclusion of what was fair and reasonable, that analysis did not determine the answer to the question. It was at most an area of expert evidence which might assist the arbitrator or the court in arriving at the answer of what is a fair and reasonable extension of time in the circumstances.

4.18.4 Ramsey J accepted as well founded the Arbitrator's finding that the Connect Project was not best suited to analysis by the Critical Path Method.

4.19 Programmes have a limited role in proving the necessary elements of causation in law. They are important in proving the initial condition necessary for the issue of causation

---

[22] HH Judge Wilcox in *Skanska Construction UK Ltd v Eggar (Barony) Ltd* [2004] EWHC 1748 .

to arise at all, in identifying the critical path and in identifying situations of concurrency. Programmes have limited use in identifying a dominant cause. Programmes are of little assistance in considerations of fairness, values judgments of the particular obligation, allocation of risk and common sense which are part of the Principled Approach.

4.2 THE INFERENCE OF CONTINUITY

4.20   Since construction projects are human endeavours, the general inference can be made that efforts will usually be directed to achieving and maintaining the planned progress and sequence of activities. This is part of the usual organisation of the project.

4.21   If an event occurs which causes delay to an operation, then it is a proper inference that the delay will have a continuing effect and delay the planned progress, subject to evidence to the contrary.

4.22   Hicks J recognised this inference of continuity in *Ascon Contracting Limited v Alfred McAlpine Construction Isle of Man Limited* [1999] (TCC).

    4.22.1   Hicks J observed that the inference, at least over short periods, was tacitly assumed in all negotiations, arbitrations and litigation of delay claims.

    4.22.2   Hicks J observed that the probability of continuity at all, or even to some extent, is likely to diminish with the passage of time and the complexity of intervening events. If there were any direct evidence that the other activities did not proceed in accordance with the planned sequence, then this would contradict the inference.

4.23   The concept of the inference of continuity is useful in emphasising the requirement to examine the effect of an event on actual progress. Even if a delay has occurred as analysed on the relevant programme at the time, the logic of the programme may change as events unfold and the analysis may no longer be accurate or valid as an analysis of the resulting causes of delay to completion or as an analysis of the contractor's prolongation costs. In particular, intervening events may subsume the previous causes of delay and alter the critical path to completion.

4.24   The fact that an event had a continuing effect may not be sufficient if the steps taken to reduce the consequences are considered insufficient. In *Mirant Asia-Pacific Construction (Hong Kong) Limited v Ove Arup and Partners International Limited* [2007]EWHC918(TCC) there was a problem with the foundations to the boiler on a power station.

    4.24.1   The absence of any critical path analysis to assist the management of the project meant that there was no appreciation at the time that any delay in finding a solution might increase the risk of delaying the project as a whole.

    4.24.2   Toulmin J found that if the remedial works had proceeded with the necessary degree of urgency they would have been completed at or close to the time on the then planned programme.

4.24.3   Accordingly, he held that the movement of the boiler foundations was not the dominant cause or even a dominant cause of the continuing and increasing delay to the project, nor did it contribute materially to the loss arising out of the delay to the project.

4.3 IDENTIFYING THE CONSTRUCTION LOGIC

4.25   Although causation in law is not simply a matter of logic, any delay analysis must be logically accurate if it is to have any weight as evidence.

4.26   Logic is based on inference and induction from uniformity of sequence between two events, but it is a logical fallacy to infer the construction logic solely from the timing of the operations. Frequently the inference is made that because an activity commenced on or near the date when a previous activity completed, that there is some logic connection between the activities and that commencement is dependent on the completion of the previous activity.   That is an example of the logical fallacy identified by Salmon LJ in *Quinn v Burch Bros Builders Ltd* [1966]CA 2 QB 370 as "*post hoc ergo propter hoc*". The actual sequence of two events may have less to do with construction logic, but more dictated by the management decision on the allocation of resources. Something more is required than the coincidence of completion and start of activities to establish the construction logic.

4.27   Inferences of logic from generalities, statistics or averages may also lead to inaccuracies. The test for the accuracy of the construction logic is its correlation with the facts as demonstrated by the judgment of His Honour Judge Hicks QC in *Ascon Contracting Limited v Alfred McAlpine Construction Isle of Man Limited* [1999] (TCC).

4.27.1   Ascon sought to prove that water ingress caused 22 days delay. The issue was the obligation to complete by a specified date. The essential fact was that after each incident of water ingress, time had to be spent salt-washing and mud-clearing before pouring of concrete could proceed.

4.27.2   Ascon relied exclusively on the evidence of an expert, but there were flaws in the expert's logic. Ascon's expert relied on a planned programme that required an average of one concrete pour per day. The inference by the expert from the average was that there was to be one pour on each day. That is not a logical inference that can be made from an average. Without more, it is equally possible for there to be no pours on some days and more than one pour on others, still leading to an average of one pour per day.

4.27.3   Ascon's expert then inferred that the water ingress prevented the concrete pour on that day if two facts could be demonstrated:

4.27.3.1 If there was not a pour on a day and

4.27.3.2 if there was water ingress on the day before, or before any pour started.

4.27.4   Although not referred to in such terms by Hicks J, this was an example of the logical fallacy in the assumption that if one event happens after another, then the first must be the cause of the second ("*post hoc ergo propter hoc*") Salmon LJ in *Quinn v Burch Bros Builders Ltd* [1966]CA 2 QB 370. Without more, the fact that a pour did not start on a particular day did not mean that the water ingress prevented the pour. The coincidence of events does not prove the logic link. There could be a number of other reasons for a pour not taking place on a particular day. If the pour was not planned for that day at all, then the incidence of water ingress was irrelevant to progress. If the preparations necessary for a pour had not been completed in time, such as formwork or reinforcement or the arrangements for delivery of concrete, or if there was simply a shortage of labour, then this would raise issues of dominant cause or concurrency.

4.27.5   Ascon's expert also sought to prove causation by accumulating from daywork sheets all the time spent by operatives on salt-washing and mud-clearing and converting that cumulative time to working days delay due to water ingress. Hicks J identified three points which he considered demonstrated the lack of logic in that approach and again the basis of the approach was the evidence of the actual progress of the works.

4.27.6   The first point of the analysis by Hicks J was based on the absence of evidence of any commensurate delay to other workforce. He observed that the cleaning operatives were only a small part of the workforce. He considered as a matter of logic the cleaning time could only have delayed the project as a whole if it was assumed that the other operatives were idle in the cleaning period, so that the project did not progress. The evidence showed that this was not the case.

4.27.7   Although not so stated by Hicks J, logically the one hour work by the labourers may delay completion by a commensurate period if their activity and the subsequent concrete pour are continuous and on the critical path to completion. If there were such a delay, then one would expect evidence of other workforce being short of work due to the delay, on the assumption that other work continued as planned. It appears that the basis for the analysis by Hicks J was that because there was evidence that showed to the contrary, the inference of continuing delay could not be made.

4.27.8   The second point of the analysis by Hicks J identified the assumption that any cleaning time in a day prevented progress by the same period on that day. Hicks J recognised that the cleaning time could be made up by working extra hours and that there was evidence that this was the practice. A programme timescale that is not continuous 24 hours 7 days per week will always be susceptible to inaccuracy if the actual hours worked are outside the timescale. A delay of one hour in an 8 hour shift will not cause delay to overall completion if the delay is made up by working overtime on the day. Unless the programme allows for the adjustment, then it will be inaccurate. In terms of overall delay and indirect prolongation costs, the extra hours worked may be considered mitigation of any delay. In terms of the direct cost of carrying out the work, the extra hours will have cost implications for the contractor.

Productivity will be reduced because of the effect of extended day on the workforce. There will also be a change in the earned income/cost ratio due to premium payment for overtime.

4.27.9   The third point of the analysis by Hicks J identified the assumption that the activity of concrete pour on the project was divisible. The evidence showed to the contrary that a concrete pour had to be started and completed on the same day. It could not be delayed by part of a day. It was either not delayed at all and started and completed on the day as planned, albeit by late working, or its was postponed and a day was lost.

4.27.10 Hicks J therefore derived no assistance from the Expert. Instead, he was left to his own analysis. He decided that it was inherently likely that despite late working there was some delay and proceeded to award a reduced extension of time.

4.4 DELAY ANALYSIS AS EVIDENCE

4.28   Commercially available software allows many activities to be recorded and analysed, in the form of readily understood programmes. The software creates a mathematical model in which activities are represented by durations and the dependence on other activities represented by time constrained links. The assumptions in the model and the inherent limitations on the way the links represent construction logic must not affect the validity of the model, particularly when events cause methods of construction to be changed, otherwise the model will be inaccurate. Available software also allows the modelling of the constraints of available resources and optimisation for efficient working, but this is not easily represented on a programme analysis.

4.29   There are many methods of analysis of delay. The choice of the appropriate analysis depends upon the evidence available, the existing programme evidence and the particular circumstances. The analysis must be based on the facts and the evidence as demonstrated in *Great Eastern Hotel Company Ltd v John Laing Construction Ltd* [2005] EWHC 181 (TCC).

4.29.1   The experts used different approaches to the analysis of delays and the identification of the critical path. Great Eastern's expert used an impacted as-planned programme analysis by which the project was analysed on a monthly basis to measure the impact of events as the project proceeded. The experts agreed that original programme demonstrated Laing's programme intentions at the time it was drawn and at the time the periods allocated to the activities were reasonable. Laing's expert in the main part proceeded retrospectively from an as-built programme to determine the critical path and respective periods of delay and causes. The principal critical path determined by each expert was broadly similar. The total extent of delay periods found by each expert broadly coincided.

4.29.2   The vital differences between the experts related to the route of the critical path and the causes of delay advanced by each expert.

4.29.3   Laing's was a broad-brush case that none of the delays was caused by Laing's and that such delays that may be proved was the consequence of concurrent causes such as the default of the design team to produce timely design information and the performance of the Trade Contractors.

4.29.4   HH Judge David Wilcox considered that the research and analyses of Eastern's expert were impressive and comprehensive. They were based upon the contemporary primary documentation that included computer records and timed site photographs depicting the actual progress of the demolition preparation and construction on site and the inter-relation of these activities. This data was objectively evaluated.

4.29.5   Wilcox J was less impressed by Laing's expert. Wilcox J considered that he demonstrated himself to be lacking in thoroughness in his research and unreliable by reason of his uncritical acceptance of the favourable accounts put forward by Laing. Laing's expert had no concept of his duty to the court as an independent expert. Despite seeing the photographs and material contained in Eastern expert's two reports received and read by him, totalling undermining credit and accuracy of a witnesses' account upon which he relied, Laing's expert chose not to revisit his earlier expressed views in accordance with his clear duty to the Court.

4.29.6   As to Eastern's analysis, Laing argued that the retrospective delay analysis carried out on the planned construction programme by Eastern's expert entirely ignored any and all existing concurrent causes of delay and/or other factors affecting other activities which might have caused delay to completion if, hypothetically, each of the identified critical activities had in fact been completed within the originally programmed period. Wilcox J considered this was not correct and that Eastern's expert did in fact separately and comprehensively carry out such an analysis and concluded that none was in fact critical.

4.29.7   Wilcox J found based on the evidence that there were no causes of critical delay other than those caused by Laing.

4.30   In *John Barker Construction Ltd v London Portman Hotel Ltd* [1996]83BLR31 Mr Recorder Toulson QC was required to consider the approach to be taken in analysing the entitlement to extension of time under a contract which incorporated the JCT Standard Form of Building Contract with Quantities, 1980 Edition, also incorporating the sectional completion supplement.

4.30.1   Toulson emphasised the need for logical analysis of the effect of events on planned progress shown by the programme established at the date of an acceleration agreement.

4.30.2   He held that the Architect's assessment of extension of time was fundamentally flawed because he did not carry out a logical analysis in a methodical way of the impact that the relevant matters had or were likely to have on the plaintiffs' planned programme. Instead, he made an impressionistic, rather than a calculated, assessment of the time, which he thought was reasonable for the various items individually and overall.

4.30.3 He held that the allowance that the Architect made for relevant events bore no logical or reasonable relation to the delay caused.

4.30.4 Toulson recognised that the assessment of a fair and reasonable extension involved an exercise of judgment, but held that the judgment must be fairly and rationally based. He held that the architect's determination of the extension of time was not a fair determination, nor was it based on a proper application of the provisions of the contract, and it was accordingly invalid.

4.31 Any analysis should not be overly complicated, but should properly address the issues and the facts. In *Skanska Construction UK Ltd v Egger (Barony) Ltd* [2005] EWHC 284 (TCC) His Honour Judge Wilcox observed that the Expert had prepared and served a long and complex report warranting the service of detailed responses by Skanska. A further report was served by the expert which could not be described as sensibly responsive to Skanska's report. A further report was served by Skanska indicating errors in the Expert's report. Sadly this assistance was not heeded. Indeed the Expert's opinion expressed in his report was neither supported by the pleadings or the evidence. The evidence of the expert generated a great deal of out of court time and expense and the subsequent hearing time was a red herring of little value.

4.5 PROVING THE INITIAL CONDITION

4.32 The initial condition for causation needs to be satisfied. If the event could not have affected the damage related to the particular obligation in issue, then the matter of causation does not arise.

4.33 In *Henry Boot Construction (UK) Limited v Malmaison Hotel (Manchester) Ltd* [1999]70ConLR32 Malmaison argued that Henry Boot's analysis of delay was "misconceived and flawed" because the events relied upon by Henry Boot did not in fact delay progress of the Works.

4.33.1 Malmaison argued that Henry Boot's assessment was based on a revised programme that ignored the true state of the Works at the date of issue. It also argued that the part of the works affected by the relevant events was not on the critical path and the analysis did not take into account any culpable delay on its part or actual progress at the time of the events relied upon. Malmaison also argued that the Works were delayed by other events.

4.33.2 The thrust of the defence was therefore that the impacted planned programme approach adopted by Henry Boot was not realistic and did not provide an accurate and logical analysis of delay.

4.33.3 Mr Justice Dyson agreed and held that under a JCT 80 Form Malmaison was entitled to argue that the Relevant Event was not likely to or did not cause delay for example because the items were not on the critical path.

CHAPTER 5 - CAUSATION AND PROGRAMMES

5.1. THE BAR CHART

Use of Bar Chart

5.1   The term "Bar Chart" is defined in BS 6079-2:2000 as a chart on which activities and their durations are represented by lines drawn to a common time scale[23]. The term "Gantt Chart" is a particular type of Bar Chart but in current usage, it is a name for bar charts in general[24].

5.2   The Bar Chart is a diagrammatic representation of the project shown on a time grid. It is a flexible representation tool that displays considerable information in a readily understood form. It can be used to plan and monitor the progress of the project. It can also be used to demonstrate the main time dimensions of the project either "as-planned" and/or "as-built".

5.3   The simplicity and flexibility of the Bar Chart is the reason for its extensive use. The Bar Chart does not require computers or special software and can be drawn easily by hand. Experience shows that it is the most natural representation of the project activities used by engineers and project managers. It is also used extensively in negotiations and legal proceedings. The types of activities are not limited in any way, since the Bar Chart is simply a diagrammatic representation of the work content, time and effort dimensions of the project. There is no logical restriction to the number of bars that are shown for an activity. "Multiple line-bars" are useful to show the duration of the same type of activity in different areas of the project.

5.4   The three essential dimensions of the project that are shown in a simple Bar Chart are:

5.4.1   The Project Activities. The essential activities necessary to complete the project are shown on the vertical axis. The activities therefore represent the work content dimension.

5.4.2   The Timing of Activities. Time is shown on the horizontal axis and the start of each activity is shown in the time grid. The start date therefore represents the time dimension of the project.

5.4.3   The Duration of Activities. The duration of the activity is shown as a bar from the start date. The duration of each of the activities therefore represent the effort dimension of the project.

---

[23]   BS 6079-2:2000 Paragraph 2.17.

[24]   BS 6079-2:2000 Paragraph 2.72.

5.5   The fourth dimension of the project of construction logic is not expressly depicted on the Bar Chart. As illustrated below, the three dimensions are usually based on assumed construction logic.

5.6   An example of a simple Bar Chart Programme is shown below in Figure 12.

Figure 12 – Equipment Project - Simple Bar Chart Programme

Activities \ Months	1	2	3	4	5	6	7	8	9	10	11	12
Procure Supplier	▬											
Design Equipment		▬								Completion ◆		
Fabrication			▬	▬								
Deliver Equipment						▬						
Erect Equipment									▬			
Design/Install Piles		▬	▬									
Formation SI ◆				▬								
Base Design			▬	▬								
Floor Slab						▬	▬					

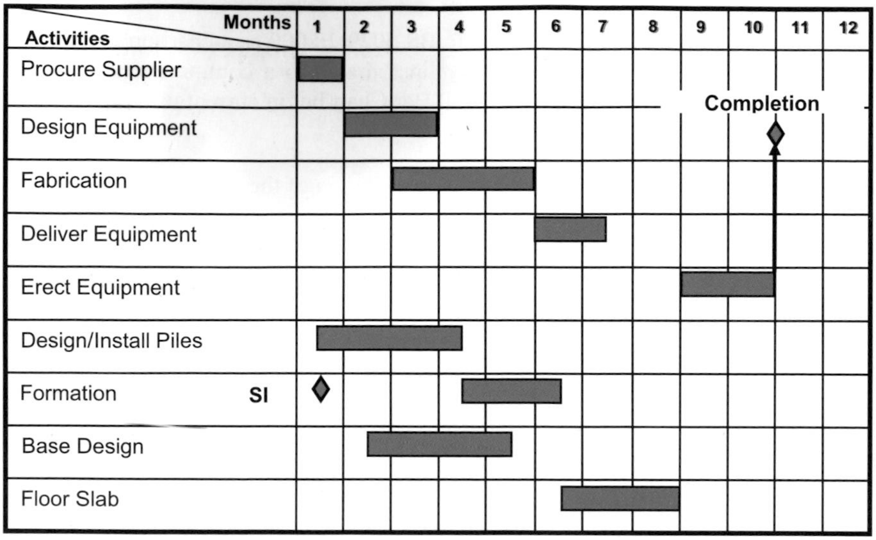

5.7   The three dimensions of the Bar Chart are common to all programmes. Any inaccuracy in the dimensions will reduce the accuracy of the programme as a model of causation. There are many possibilities for inaccuracy in the dimensions.

    5.7.1   If the Bar Chart is a plan for future work, then estimates will have been made of both the work content of the project and of each activity. The accuracy of the estimates depends upon the accuracy of the interpretation of the workscope and the forecast of the resources and timescale.

    5.7.2   If the Bar Chart is a record of the as-built work, then the start and finish of each activity may not be properly identified and therefore insufficiently accurate to infer the as-built construction logic. Without records of resources, the recorded durations may inaccurately represent continuous activity, when in fact there may be periods when no resources were used or there was no working.

5.8   The absence of the fourth dimension of construction logic means that the Bar Chart is not an adequate model to analyse the consequences on expected completion, if the actual timing or duration of an activity is not met. Therefore, for example, if an activity is started later than shown on the Bar Chart, the Bar Chart does not allow the effect on completion to be analysed, without additional information. The Bar Chart simply shows that an activity started later than planned. Similarly, if an activity requires a longer duration than shown on the Bar Chart, this only shows that an activity took longer than estimated.

5.9   The absence of logic links between activities means that the use of the Bar Chart is limited to monitoring progress rather than forward planning of the project. It is used in the initial stages of delay analysis to compare planned and actual progress so as to identify possible problem activities.

5.10   Inaccuracies in the model of causation will arise from illogical inferences made from the information in the dimensions. Although a Bar Chart does not expressly state the fourth dimension of construction logic, the other three dimensions of activities, timing and duration are all based on assumed construction logic, even in the preparation of an as-built Bar Chart.

5.11   The accuracy of the Bar Chart as a model of causation requires a detailed understanding of the engineering process involved and is examined below for each of the dimensions, illustrated using the project shown in Figure 12 Bar Chart.

Project Activities

5.12   The number and nature of the activities are as diverse as the number of projects. There is no limit to the types of projects and the types of activities. It is usual for the activities to be descriptions of physical operations and this is the definition in BS 6079-2:2000. In practice, any means of defining the project can be adopted.

       5.12.1   The activities could define the project labour as a list of trades involved such as plasterers, carpenters, plumbers and painters or a list of the subcontractors or manufacturers.

       5.12.2   In a design project, the activities could be the list of particular individuals.

       5.12.3   In a manufacture project, the activities could be a list of the individual parts of the equipment.

       5.12.4   In a system project such as a heating and ventilation system or a processing system, the activities could be a list of the each sub-system together with the testing and commissioning of each sub-system and then the whole system.

       5.12.5   The activity could be a single event "key date" which is necessary for the project but is within the control or responsibility of others such as

                5.12.5.1   the date for supply of information, or

                5.12.5.2   the date for provision of a resource such as power, materials, equipment or attendance or access or

                5.12.5.3   the date for inspections, approvals and consents.

       5.12.6   The activity could also be a single event "milestone" that marks the date of completion of a number of operations by the contractor such as "power-on" after testing and commissioning, or "weather-tight", or "sectional completion" or "handover". The milestone may mark the date of acceptance of the project or part by the Employer.

5.13 The activities can be a combination of any of the above types. The flexibility by which the work content dimension can be presented means that the Bar Chart can be used by anyone with an understanding of the enterprise and explains its widespread use.

5.14 If the activity is an operation as opposed to a resource or a machinery part, then the description on the Bar Chart will usually be insufficient on its own to accurately define the work content, which will be derived from the context of the full list of activities as well as the terms of the contract. If the list of activities is incomplete then the Bar Chart will not be an accurate model of the project. Important essential activities, often ignored, are those within the control of others such as the periods for the approvals and consents of the Employer. The periods for approval may be fixed by the terms of the Contract.

5.15 The list of activities and the descriptions is a statement, albeit limited, of the method adopted in carrying out the project. They must be sufficient and complete to be an accurate representation of the project.

5.16 In the example project in Figure 12 the project is the design and manufacture of an item of equipment, the construction of a piled foundation and base and the erection of the equipment on the base. The activities are listed on the vertical axis. In order to simplify the presentation and increase the utility of the Bar Chart each listed activity represents a number of discrete sub-activities, which together make up that activity. The extent of the work content for each activity requires examination of the contractor's obligations to the Employer, which will be determined from the contract terms and conditions including specifications and drawings. A particular difficulty in practice is the identification of responsibilities at key work interfaces as illustrated below for the simple Bar Chart at Figure 12.

5.17 In the example in Figure 12, the activities for the manufacture and delivery of the equipment are of varying types. The work is to be subcontracted to a supplier manufacturer, so that not all the activities are directly under the control of the contractor, but controlled indirectly through the mechanisms of the supply sub-contract.

5.17.1 Procure Supplier: The work content of activity "Procure Supplier" includes the activities of preparation of tender documents, identification of possible tenderers, the review of tenders received, possible negotiations, the conclusion of the sub-contract and the issue of the order for the equipment. The work content may also include applications to the Employer for approval of the list of intended suppliers and approval of the terms of the subcontract if so prescribed under the contract.

5.17.2 Design Equipment: The activity work content of "Design Equipment" is carried out by the supplier, but may require the Employer to provide technical interface information such as system loads or performance profile of other equipment, so that the contractor can instruct the supplier. The work content may also include obtaining approvals of or certificates for the design by third parties or the Employer.

5.17.3 Fabrication: The activity work content of "Fabrication" is carried out by the supplier, but may require the Employer to supply particular parts. The work content may also include inspections and approvals by the Employer, test certificates by others and the preparation and supply of maintenance and operation manuals.

5.17.4 Deliver Equipment: The activity work content of "Deliver Equipment" will include the activities of loading at the factory, transport to site and unloading at the site. The work content may include temporary storage on site and the provision of security and protection until the equipment is erected in its final position. The division of responsibility between the supplier and contractor will be determined by the terms of the supplier sub-contract. Whether or not the Employer has any responsibility will depend on the terms of the contract, which may specify the division of responsibilities for any clearance through customs, licences for transport on public highways and attendance at site.

5.17.5 Erect Equipment: The activity work content of "Erect Equipment" will include placing the equipment in its final position and may include connection of any holding down bolts and any grouting necessary, any connection to the required power supplies and any testing of the equipment.

5.18 In Figure 12, the activities for the design and construction of the base are also of varying types.

5.18.1 Design/Install Piles: The activity "Design/Install Piles" comprises two distinct albeit related sub-activities of design and site installation.

The work content of the sub-activity of pile design will require examination of the information on the nature and properties of the ground, identification of the loads required to be transmitted to the piles over the specified design life, the distribution of loads to each pile, the selection of the type and size of the piles as well as the preparation of calculations and drawings for the piles. The Employer may have specified the type of piles and may be required to supply site information, borehole investigations and test results. The work content may also include obtaining approvals of or certificates for the design by third parties or the Employer.

The work content of the sub-activity of installation of piles will require order and delivery of piles if steel or prefabricated concrete, the order of materials such as concrete and reinforcement if bored cast in-situ piles and the transport and set-up of equipment to install the piles. The list of activities does not identify separately the construction of a pile cap, so that if it is part of the project work content it may be part of this activity or part of the activity "Floor

Slab". The work content may also include inspections and approvals by the Employer and may include load tests on piles.

5.18.2 <u>Base Design</u>: The work content of the activity "Base Design" will require examination of the information on the nature and properties of the ground and the identification of the loads and usage over the specified design life. The Employer may have specified particular items or features to be incorporated or accommodated in the Base and these may require interface details to allow them to be included in the design. The work content may also include obtaining approvals of or certificates for the design by third parties or the Employer.

5.18.3 <u>Formation</u>: The work content of the activity "Formation" requires earthworking activities that may simply require levelling of the area ready for the floor slab, but may require some excavation and imported fill with the resulting approvals and certificates.

5.18.4 <u>Floor Slab</u>: The work content of the activity "Floor Slab" will include the order of materials such as concrete and reinforcement and may also include delivery from others or the Employer of items to be incorporated in the slab. The work content may also include inspections and approvals by the Employer

5.19 In Figure 12, the "key date" of "SI" is a single event activity that identifies the supply of site information. The extent of the site information required will be dictated by the design and the contractor's method of working and may include geological information, borehole logs, laboratory tests of samples, insitu tests and water tests. The extent of the responsibility of the Employer for obtaining and providing the site information will be defined by the terms of the contract.

5.20 In Figure 12, the "milestone" of "Completion" is also a single event activity that marks the date of completion of the project. The milestone is shown as dictated by the final sub-activity in the activity "Erect Equipment" which may be physical completion of the erection or may be determined by a successful test and final approval or acceptance by the Employer.

Timing of Activities

5.21 Absolute time is continuous and regular 24 hours per day and 7 days per week. The absolute timescale is used for continuous shift working on projects involving tunnelling operations or concreting operations where absolute continuity of working is an essential part of the method of working. The absolute timescale may also be used on emergency works.

5.22 Frequently the absolute timescale is not used as the timescale for the Bar Chart grid but instead the "working day" or "working week" is adopted. The "working day" and the "working week" are usually defined as the "site hours" under the construction contract. In the UK site hours are commonly between 07:30hrs and 17:30hrs Monday to Friday and 07:30hrs to 13:00hrs on Saturday. Work outside these hours may require special arrangements and probably require payment of a premium for overtime.

5.23   The same measure of time is usually adopted throughout the Bar Chart, even though that may not be accurate for each activity. On the same project, the "working day" may be different for different activities. If the Bar Chart is to accurately model the project then the effect of different working days and the effect of working overtime need to be incorporated in the model. If the overall timescale does not allow such local analysis, then this may be achieved by separate analysis in a sub-network Bar Chart.

5.24   An activity that is a "key date" or a "milestone" has no duration, but is a date marking an event. Such an activity does not measure effort but is used as a means of monitoring or recording the completion of a number of activities. It may be used to mark the commencement of other activities such as an access key date which marks the commencement of construction by the contractor or others, or a stage milestone which marks an obligation of the Employer to make a stage payment, or a completion milestone which marks the commencement of obligations in the defects liability period and the release of part of retention.

5.25   The start date of each activity, together with the list of activities and the descriptions, allows inferences to be made as to the method adopted in carrying out the project. The inferences are not sufficient without more to ensure that the implied method of working is an accurate representation of the project.

5.26   In order to make inferences of construction logic from the coincidence of dates something more than the coincidence is required. General construction knowledge may be all that is required, but specific technical information of the actual design and construction details and the limitation of operation of plant and other resources is usually required.

5.27   There is usually a relationship between the different parts of the project designs. The information of the incidence and frequency of loads and capacity resulting from one part of the design, will often be required for other parts of the design. The continuity of the design resource, progressing from one part of the design to another is also a common factor in the timing of design activities. The relationship is often dealt with by sequential timing of activities without express identification of the construction logic.

5.28   In the example in Figure 12, the timescale is shown on the horizontal axis in "months". This is not usually a sufficiently accurate timescale since the number of days in each month varies, unless "months" is intended to be to a four week period. The usual timescale is weeks with the commencement date for the week also shown. The timescale of working week and working hours to accurately model the activities will be different for the activities of design, fabrication and site works being respectively office, factory and construction site. The timescale to accurately model the activity "Deliver Equipment" is likely to be the absolute timescale involving as it does transportation. The approval periods specified in contracts are usually stated as calendar days. If the Bar Chart is to be an accurate model of the project then it is necessary to choose the overall timescale that will accommodate all the differences.

5.29   In the example in Figure 12 there is no express statement of logic that allows identification of those activity start dates which are dependent on or driven by the activities in other activities. Inferences can be made of the method of working from the coincidence of dates, activity descriptions and general construction practice. Such inferences may be logical fallacies of causation, so the assumptions and the evidence for the inferences need to be carefully considered. The illustrations below show that in order to make accurate inferences of the constraints of the methods of working, the technical details of the work content of all activities need to be considered together with the physical and resource constraints.

5.29.1   <u>Procure Supplier</u>: The start date of the activity "Procure Supplier" is the start of the contract with the Employer. This type of event is defined in BS 6079-2:2000 as a "start event" being an event with succeeding but no preceding activities[25]. There is no means of identifying on the Bar Chart whether or not it is necessary for the activity to start at that date to achieve the contract completion date. If the Bar Chart is a plan for future working, the immediate start of the activity infers that the contractor considers it is necessary for the equipment supplier to be identified early in the project. This would appear to be common sense given the nature of the project, but there is no express logic that identifies the subsequent activities dependant on that selection to allow an inference of the critical date for selection.

5.29.2   <u>Design Equipment</u>: The coincidence of the finish of the activity "Procure Supplier" and the start of the activity "Design Equipment" allows the initial inference that the design will not be carried out until the supplier has been procured. That inference is consistent with common sense, but may not be an accurate representation of the project. As the equipment begins to be more accurately defined during the supplier procurement process, the Contractor may require the Employer to make choices and provide clarifications of his requirements that are a necessary part of the design process. Although the design by the Supplier may not take place until an order is issued, the Employer may already have been involved in earlier design decisions with the resulting possible risks of delay.

5.29.3   <u>Fabrication</u>: General construction knowledge allows the inference to be made that the activities of "Design Equipment" and "Fabrication" are interconnected. The further inference is that it is necessary to design some part of the equipment (even if only selection of a prefabricated part) before a start can be made on fabrication and that is shown on the Bar Chart with the different start dates for the two activities. The start date of the activity "Fabrication" is before the finish date for the activity "Design Equipment" which allows the further inference that not all the design is required to be completed before fabrication can start. This is an example of phased design/contract that is a common feature of construction. The Bar Chart does not expressly state the extent and nature of design that must be carried out before fabrication can start and that cannot be inferred from the Bar Chart; something more is required.

---

[25]   BS 6079-2:2000 Paragraph 2.168.

5.29.4 Deliver Equipment: The activity "Deliver Equipment" has a start date following immediately from the finish of the activity "Fabrication". The inference may be made that delivery cannot commence until fabrication is completed. If all of the Equipment is to be assembled as part of the fabrication, because either it is a single unit or to ensure fit or for performance testing of the whole, then that may be an accurate inference. If on the other hand the assembly is part of the activity "Deliver Equipment" or the activity "Erect Equipment", then delivery can commence as soon as parts are fabricated and the inference is not accurate. In that case, there may be a number of commercial reasons for the incidence of dates. For example, the decision may be to reduce the cost of delivery, or to simplify the assembly on site by sequential delivery and assembly of parts. The decision may be based on perceptions of risk and liability for example to avoid long storage periods on site of parts of the Equipment because of difficulties of security or because of concerns as to transfer of risk of damage and ownership.

5.29.5 SI: The activity key date "SI" is a date after commencement of the contract with the Employer. If the Bar Chart is a plan for future working then it may be that such a date marks the specified obligation in the contract for the Employer to supply the information, but it may only be the contractor's estimate of the required date for information to allow the completion date to be achieved.

The assumption may be that there is no need for the contractor to obtain any additional information other than that available and provided by the Employer. The accuracy of the assumption will depend on the information available. The accuracy of the assumption may also depend on the interpretation of the contract; whether the contractor discharges his obligations under the contract if he designs in accordance with the information provided.

5.29.6 Design/Install Piles: The start date of the activity "Design/Install Piles" is the same as the activity key date "SI". The inference that the site information must be provided before the design of piles can commence is unlikely to be accurate. Some design can be carried out on loads and layout based on preliminary views of the ground conditions, although this will need to be reviewed and if necessary, the design revised when the site information is provided. The design of piles cannot be completed without the site information so the start date may simply reflect the contractor's choice of economic design activity without the need for preliminary views, reviews and design revisions.

5.29.7 Base Design: It is difficult to make any inferences for the start date for the activity "Base Design" since it does not appear to be coincident with the start or finish of any other activities. Any inferences of construction logic would be made from the content and nature of the designs.

5.29.8 Formation: The activity "Formation" has a start date following immediately from the finish of the activity "Design/Install Piles". The inference may be made that the formation cannot be prepared until piling is completed. The inference is consistent with general construction knowledge if formation is only levelling the area ready for the floor slab, with local excavation and fill.

If a wider area of excavation and filling is required, then it is more likely that such work would be carried out before the piling because of the difficulties of earthworks plant working around piles.

5.29.9 <u>Floor Slab</u>: The activity "Floor Slab" has a start date following immediately from the finish of the activity Formation". The inference may be made that the floor slab cannot be constructed until the formation is completed. The inference is consistent with general construction knowledge, since the floor slab is required to be constructed on the formation. A phased construction may be possible, but that requires further technical information.

5.29.10 <u>Erect Equipment</u>: The activity "Erect Equipment" starts some time after the finish of the activity "Deliver Equipment". The inference to be made from the activity descriptions and the start dates is that the Equipment is to be stored at site for a period after fabrication and that there may be a requirement for security and protection until the equipment is erected. The Bar Chart does not expressly describe such an activity and an inference of responsibility cannot be inferred from the Bar Chart. The activity "Erect Equipment" has a start date following immediately from the finish of the activity "Floor Slab". The inference may be made that the equipment cannot be erected until the floor slab is completed. The inference is consistent with general construction knowledge, since the equipment must be constructed on the floor slab.

5.29.11 <u>Completion</u>: The activity milestone "completion" is the only activity that is shown as dictated by the final sub-activity of another activity, which in this case is in the activity "Erect Equipment". That is achieved by expressly stating a link between the two activities.

Duration of Activities

5.30 The duration of an activity may be determined by the period between two dates, such as the period required after placing of concrete for the concrete cubes to reach a minimum strength. The contract may prescribe a period, such as the period for the duration of a particular test or for example the period to be allowed for the Employer to respond to a submission. Such an activity does not measure effort by the contractor but records the time that must be allocated to the activity.

5.31 The duration of an activity that is a time risk contingency is fixed by the contractor to allow for the incidence of the risk allocated under the contract. The accuracy of the contingency depends upon the correctness of the Contractor's interpretation of the contract allocation of risk and the accuracy of the estimate of the extent and consequences of the risk event. Usually a Contractor will make a time risk contingency by reducing anticipated productivity to allow for the possible incidence of the risk event, thereby increasing the duration of the activity. In that case, the time risk contingency is not shown as a separate activity.

5.32 Apart from the above types of activities, the duration of an activity will measure the effort involved in terms of resources, material, plant and energy. The accuracy of the duration depends on the accuracy of the activity completion date. If the Bar Chart represents the future plan for the project then the duration will be an estimate and may or may not be accurate. This will depend upon the assumptions made as to productivity and the time risk contingency allowed in the duration. If the Bar Chart represents the as-built progress of the project, the actual completion is not easily identified. In practice, effort on an activity naturally tails off, so that small items of work may be left incomplete to be dealt with as part of a snagging list.

5.33   It is not accurate, without more, to infer from a continuous unbroken bar that the effort is continuous. The resource level shown on a planned programme as continuous may only be an average. The activity may not involve continuous activity.

    5.33.1   The activity will always comprise a sub-network of activities, which may not be continuous, nor in sequence. The greater the work scope of the activity the more diverse will be the sub-activities. The greater the diversity of sub-activities the more likely that the activity bar will not comprise continuous effort of the same type of resource.

    5.33.2   Even if the sub-activities in an activity are continuous during working, the activity bar may not involve continuous use of the resource. There may be "non-working" periods. The duration may include periods when resources are not working on the activity at all; either allocated to other activities or are "standing" awaiting the passage of time such as curing of concrete and such as the passage of weather that prevents working. Even if the same types of resource are allocated throughout the duration, there may be different levels of resources at different times.

5.34   Often the finish and therefore the duration of an activity will be defined by the construction logic, which constrains the start of the subsequent activity. In some cases the completion is defined by a deliverable object such as a document and in others by a stage of design or construction. The "finish" of the same activity may be different depending on the context. These aspects are illustrated below for the activities in Figure 12 above.

    5.34.1   Procure Supplier: The deliverable object which marks the completion of the work content of the activity "Procure Supplier" is the formality of either the issue of an order or the execution of an agreement or the acceptance of the tender. The formality marks the completion of procurement and the creation of the legal relationship. That may not be the event that marks completion for follow-on activity of "Design Equipment". It is a common occurrence in construction that work is commenced before completion of the formality, sometimes by the issue of a letter of intent and often with only an oral instruction to commence. The formal conclusion of procurement may never occur and may in any event be different to the completion that allows the follow-on design.

    The activity does not involve continuous resource effort by the contractor. There are fixed time periods when there is no activity by the contractor awaiting return of tenders. As described above there may also be periods required for approval by the Employer of the lists of intended suppliers and approval of the terms of the intended subcontract. A prudent contractor may allow a time contingency for possible delay by tenderers particularly on such an important activity of the project. The absolute timescale is likely to be appropriate to accurately depict the duration.

Different resources, technical, legal and commercial, are likely to be involved at different times.

5.34.2 Design Equipment: There are likely to be several stages of the design in the activity "Design Equipment" which allow follow-on activities to commence, as each stage is completed. The identification of prefabricated parts may allow those parts to be purchased before completion of the whole design. If the design includes structural, mechanical and electrical design, then the structural design may be completed at an early stage when the main parts have been sized allowing the fabrication to commence. The systems design may therefore be carried out as fabrication on the main parts is being carried out. The completion shown on the Bar Chart does not therefore mark completion for all follow-on activities.

Different resources may be used for each part of the design from different engineering disciplines. Although the supplier's resources are involved, the contractor will be involved in making interface decisions and the duration may also include periods for approval of the design by the Employer and/or obtaining certificates from third parties.

The duration and completion of the activity described on the Bar Chart as a single continuous bar may not accurately model the progress of the work. In any delay analysis sub-division of the activity into relevant sub-activities is likely.

The appropriate timescale to accurately model duration is likely to be the working hours of the main design office.

5.34.3 Fabrication: The completion of the activity "Fabrication" for the follow-on activity "Delivery" depends on the method of assembly as described above, and whether delivery can be piecemeal or as one unit. The completion of fabrication for final stage payment may not be the physical completion of fabrication but the supply of maintenance and operation manuals.

The main resources involved in the activity "Fabrication" are those of the supplier, but the contractor may be involved in obtaining Employer's approvals and third party certificates.

The appropriate timescale to accurately model duration is likely to be the working hours of the fabrication site.

5.34.4 Deliver Equipment: Completion of the activity "Deliver Equipment" may be defined by the contract as delivery to a ship or as delivery to a port or as delivery to the installation site or as the delivery of necessary papers and clearance certificates. The completion will be prescribed by the contract division of responsibilities for clearance through customs, licences for transport on public highways and attendance at site. The completion of the activity "Delivery" for the follow-on activity of "Erection" depends on the method of assembly, whether at the manufacture site or the installation site.

Various resources are likely to be involved in the activity "Deliver Equipment" such as craneage and transport as well as labour. The contractor may be involved in obtaining Employer's approvals and third party certificates.

The absolute timescale is likely to be appropriate to accurately model duration.

5.34.5   SI: The key date of "SI" assumes that all the information is provided as a single event. That is likely if the documentary information had already been compiled before the contract start date. If the information is being obtained by documentary search or ground investigation or through tests, different types of site information may be obtained or provided progressively.

There

If the information available is not sufficient, it may be necessary to obtain site information during construction to verify the assumptions made in the design.

The contractor's resources involved in the activity "SI" depends on the terms of the contract and whether or not the various designs are required to be based solely on the information provided or whether the contractor is required to obtain any further information necessary to ensure that the project achieves its purpose.

The effective completion of the activity "SI" for the purpose of start of the activity "Design/Install Piles" may be different to that for the start of the activity "Base Design" since each may require different site information.

5.34.6   Design/Install Piles: The duration of the activity "Design/Install Piles" covers a broad range of activities involving different timescales for design and site resources, for the Employer's approval procedures as well as third parties in ground investigations and possibly absolute periods for pile testing. It is likely that a sub-network of the various sub-activities would be required to accurately model the sub-activities with different timescales.

There will be different effective completion dates for different follow-on activities, depending upon the completion date for the relevant sub-activity of the activity "Design/Install Piles".

5.34.7   Base Design: There are two aspects of the design in the activity "Base Design" - the design of the formation including any drainage and the design of the floor slab. The completion date for the follow-on activities of "Formation" and "Floor Slab" are likely to be different. The appropriate timescale to accurately model duration is likely to be the working hours of the main design office.

5.34.8   Formation: The activity "Formation" is a site based activity so that the timescale will be the site working hours. The completion of the activity for the start of the follow-on activity "Floor Slab" is likely to be physical completion of the earthworks, unless there is phased construction allowing an overlap of work.

5.34.9   <u>Floor Slab</u>: The completion of the activity "Floor Slab" will be the date when the concrete achieves the design strength and the formwork has been removed. The completion for the start of the follow-on activity "Erect Equipment" is likely to be physical completion of the work with an absolute period to allow the concrete to achieve the minimum cube strength to allow the floor slab to start taking load. The activity "Floor Slab" is a site based activity so that the timescale will be the site working hours, unless continuous concreting is required in which case the timescale may be extended hours and may be the absolute timescale of 24 hours per day.

5.34.10   <u>Erect Equipment</u>: The completion of the activity "Erect Equipment" may be the physical completion of erecting the equipment on the floor slab, but may be specified by the contract in terms of final approval by the Employer or involve testing and commissioning with a performance test certificate. The activity is a site based activity so that the timescale will be the site working hours, unless the testing and commissioning involves continuous operation when the absolute timescale is appropriate.

5.34.11   <u>Completion</u>: The milestone "Completion" may be determined solely by the completion of the activity "Erect Equipment" In practice the activity "Completion" will involve remedying notified defects and completing parts of activities left for later. The activity will comprise a duration with a timescale of the site working hours. The actual completion may then be a final approval or a handing over certificate.

5.2. THE RESOURCE HISTOGRAM

5.35   The activity dimension of duration is a measure of effort, but requires an allocation of resource to allow a usable measure in terms of numbers or cost. The Resource Histogram is commonly used as a diagrammatic representation of resource shown on the Bar Chart.

5.36   The resource is represented as a bar in which the vertical dimension is the measure of the quantity of the resource and the horizontal dimension the period the resource is dedicated to the activity. The area encompassed by the bar represents the measure of effort in the units of the chart. If the horizontal timescale is the same as the Bar Chart, then the histogram can be shown on the Bar Chart.

5.37   The timescale for the resource depends upon the relevant timescale used to price the resource, and requires similar considerations as for the Bar Chart. The histogram may be used for labour and plant. The usual timescale for labour is "manhours" which is the basis for payment of wages, with a minimum weekly hours guaranteed if employed by the contractor and an agreement for payment of overtime. Labour is often recorded using weekly timesheets with the time spent each day recorded in hours. Sometimes the timesheets will also record build up of the hours with the time allocated to each activity. Plant may also be recorded in the same way, but usually the timescale is a day which records the allocation of plant to the particular site. The plant allocation sheets may unusually record when plant is working and therefore using fuel and other consumables and when it is standing. The differences in timescale are taken into account by factoring the hourly or daily costs to arrive at a unit cost for the timescale used on the grid.

5.38   The resource may be defined in terms of overall resource, or separated by type of resource such as design and site or separated by trade. Most often resource is shown in terms of expenditure, which allows different resources with different costs and different timescales to be accumulated to provide a single measure of overall effort.

5.39   An example of a Resource Histogram is shown below in Figure 13 using the first three activities in the Figure 12 Bar Chart.

Figure 13 – Resource Histogram

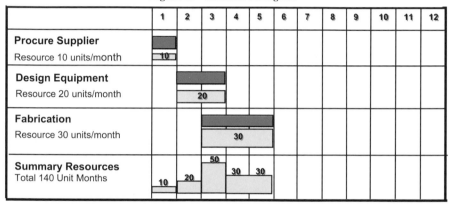

5.40   The resources for each of the above three activities are different, but are shown on the histogram in terms of the universal units of cost per month. In that way the overall cashflow can be represented. The histogram therefore includes allocations of working hours per labour per month and the working days for plant per month which may not be accurately represented by the continuous unbroken bar for the timescale.

5.3. THE PLANNED PROGRAMME

5.41   The use of the "Planned Programme" as the starting point for delay analysis has the following advantages:

5.41.1   The planned programme is evidence of the expectations of the Contractor and possibly the Employer at the commencement of the project.

5.41.2   The planned programme is evidence of the context in which decisions were made, particularly in relation to mitigation.

5.41.3   The planned programme is likely to have been used and referred to during the project and therefore allows better understanding of other evidence.

5.41.4   The comparison of planned programme and actual events allows an initial estimate of possible delays to activities.

5.42   An essential part of the planned programme is the record of the estimates on which durations and timing are based, if it is to be effective in delay analysis.

5.43   It is not always easy to identify the appropriate "Planned Programme" for delay analysis.

5.44   The Contractor's agreement with an Employer to carry out a project is usually based on a view of how the work will be carried out. The plan may not be set out in the agreement as a programme, but may be part of a tender or produced during negotiations. Frequently a programme is prepared at commencement of the project either as part of the contractor's obligations or simply to assist the contractor to manage the project. All such programmes are evidence of how the Contractor planned to carry out the project at that time. The plan is an express statement and demonstrates the understanding of the workscope and of the Contractor's obligations and the decisions he has made.

5.44.1   The plan may demonstrate the decision on the method of procurement, whether by direct labour or by subcontract.

5.44.2   The plan may demonstrate the construction logic, expressly or by inference, for the chosen method of construction through the timing of activities.

5.44.3   The plan may demonstrate the deployment of resources through the durations of the activities.

5.45   The issued tender programme is a high level programme produced to demonstrate to the Employer that the tenderer has understood the workscope and to describe to the Employer the proposed method of working. The main purpose of the issued tender programme is to allow the Employer to make comparisons with proposals by other tenderers and to assist in selection. Frequently the tender programme is prepared in a very short and intensive period where the emphasis is more on showing compliance and achieving a competitive price, rather than an accurate time analysis of the project.

5.46   The programme prepared at commencement of the project is more carefully considered than the tender programme and usually more detailed. Such a programme may for the first time include the views of those responsible for carrying out the project rather than the estimators at tender stage. As the project progresses revised programmes may be issued. Frequently short duration programmes are issued for immediate tasks as one week or two week "look-ahead" programmes. The look-ahead programmes are likely to be very detailed but limited to the immediate activities.

5.47   The initial planned programme is only one model of the way in which the works could proceed. The initial plan may be incorrect, either under- or over-estimating productivity or durations or the effects of risk events. Some changes to the planned progress will not be the result of external factors but of the inaccuracies inherent in the planned programme. Whenever one assumption in the planned programme is shown to be inaccurate by actual events, other similar assumptions may need to be revised.

5.48   A programme is not always reliable evidence of the contractor's plan. The programme may be ill considered and not accurately model the resources on which the contractor's prices were based. It may not accurately model the method of working described by the contractor in other documents. In that case, the prepared programme must be re-constructed if it is properly to be called a "Planned Programme".

5.49   The reconstructed planned programme needs to be carefully prepared if it is to be an accurate baseline for analysis. In *Skanska Construction UK Ltd v Eggar (Barony) Ltd* [2004] EWHC 1748 a networked planned programme was reconstructed from a programme used in the contract, but one of the vital activities was misinterpreted and a activity was omitted. Milestone dates were added which were incorrect. The construction programme recast by the expert identified two critical paths passing through two zones. Since each zone had its own process entry and practical completion dates, there was a compelling inference that other critical paths existed which had not been considered by the expert. In addition, the relevant baseline programme selected by the expert for impact analysis became virtually redundant almost from the outset because of the late provision of vital information. HH Judge Wilcox held that the programme was not reliable as a baseline.

5.50   Even if the plan accurately records the contractor's intentions, the estimates on which it is based may be inaccurate. The interpretation of the contractor's obligations may be wrong. The assumptions as to the design may be incorrect. There may be inadequate allowance for the contract allocation of risk.

5.51   The inaccuracies may mean that the contractor's planned programme if followed without change, would not have allowed the Contractor to comply with his obligations under the contract. The "Planned Programme" may have an in-built delay to the contract completion.

5.52   Even if the initial programme accurately records the intentions of the Contractor at commencement of the project, it may not do so later in the project, particularly when the relevant event occurs which is the subject of the delay analysis.

5.53   A later programme is likely to be a more accurate assessment of the project than an earlier programme and is evidence of the accuracy or inaccuracy of earlier programmes. There will be increasingly more accurate information about the project with time and greater cumulative effort will have been expended analysing the project. There will be specific performance indicators available and a greater understanding of the project. Later estimates of future performance are likely to be more accurate. This is particularly so where the future is not distant as in the two week look-up programmes.

5.54   Even if there is no express programme available at commencement of the project, the contractor will have a plan on which his prices are based and in order to organise and allocate labour, plant and equipment. That information will allow a "Planned Programme" to be re-constructed.

5.4. THE AS-BUILT PROGRAMME

5.55   The as-built programme may be prepared in one of two ways:

5.55.1   The planned programme may be updated during the progress of the project, updating the list of activities, durations, timing and logic.   The final programme will be the as-built programme.   Each update will itself be evidence to be used in the delay analysis. Even if the planned programme is regularly updated to record actual progress during the project, further information will usually be required to prepare an accurate as-built programme for delay analysis.

5.55.2   The as-built programme may be constructed by a retrospective analysis of all the available evidence. The management of information to provide accurate as-built data requires considerable effort, so that inevitably all the required data will not be available.

5.56   The use of the "As-Built Programme" as the starting point for delay analysis has the following advantages:

5.56.1   The analysis is based on actual events, durations and sequences and can be used for issues such as extension of time, prolongation costs and disruption.

5.56.2   The context in which an event occurred and decisions made can be accurately modelled.

5.56.3   The evidence of actual timing and duration of activities and activities allows the actual construction logic to be verified.

5.57   In practice, it is necessary to focus the detailed analysis on key areas of delay instead of the whole project in order to avoid unnecessary expense. That requires an iterative method to ensure that the key areas are accurately identified.

5.58   The accuracy of the as-built programme is determined by the extent of evidence of progress, the accuracy of the evidence and the interpretation of the evidence. The facts stated in the as-built programme and selected by the expert preparing the programme, may be considered unreliable and inaccurate if the best evidence available has not been used. In some cases, the best evidence will be that of the participants closely and continuously involved with the project.

5.59   The selection of facts to be used may require an element of judgment particularly on technical matters and when faced with apparently conflicting information.   The selected fact will then be an inference based on all the information available.   The judgment made must be objective and logical to be accurate and reliable. A delay analysis will be unreliable if the data included in the programme is selected and characterised by others rather than the expert, and the judgment of the others cannot be tested. It is particularly important that the expert carries out adequate research and checks the data used and has sufficient intellectual rigour to admit to the possibility of doubt when new evidence comes to light. The accuracy of the delay analysis is only as good as data input into the computer programme however impeccable the logic of that programme[26].

5.60   The weight of evidence depends upon a range of factors and is part of the essential function of the Tribunal and not the expert. There are particular difficulties when the evidence is based on the recollection of participants in the project.

    5.60.1   The personnel involved with the project for a considerable time are likely to have a deep understanding of the project, particularly the construction logic, but inaccurate recollection of dates and times.

    5.60.2   It is rare for the evidence to be accurate without documentary evidence refreshing the memory, unless the events involved are in some way remarkable and therefore memorable.

    5.60.3   Generally, the passage of time may erode the accuracy of recollection. A record of the event close in time is likely to be more accurate than a recollection some time later.

    5.60.4   The personnel managing day-to-day activities may not have an overall view of the project and may not have recognised or reported changes in the planned rate of progress or changes in the method of working.

    5.60.5   The evidence of personnel taken some time after the event may be guarded in the interests of self-protection.

    5.60.6   Unfortunately, experts who compile evidence to construct the as-built programme frequently do not have the necessary skills to take witness evidence, yet the as-built programme will usually depend on such evidence unless the expert has direct first hand knowledge.

5.61   The weight to be given to documentary evidence depends on the nature of the record and may depend upon the knowledge of the person making the record, particularly if the matter recorded involves a technical judgment or a technical appreciation of the event.

    5.61.1   Formal records prepared as part of a continuing process such as progress reports and programmes are likely to be accurate, particularly if issued to project participants on a regular basis without adverse comment.

    5.61.2   Regularly kept diaries recording the work carried out, the allocation of resources and particular incidents are likely to be accurate, particularly if keeping the diary is part of the duties of the person involved. Daily records that are generalised are unlikely to allow accurate analysis.

    5.61.3   Multiple copies of the same record on a distribution list will support the veracity of the date of the record.

---

[26]   HH Judge Wilcox in *Skanska Construction UK Ltd v Eggar (Barony) Ltd* [2004] EWHC 1748 .

5.61.4   Photographs taken by professional photographer on a regular basis will support the accuracy of the image and the date the photograph was taken.

5.61.5   Correspondence recording events at the time may also be an accurate source of evidence, although frequently self-serving.

5.61.6   Timesheets or daywork sheets signed by the Employer's representative as a true record are likely to be accurate.

5.62   Computer systems are often used to record important facts such as the issue of instructions, drawing issues, the approval of submissions, material orders and deliveries, commencement and completion of activities, allocation of resources, payments, drawing issues, quantities and rates.   The revisions of programmes maintained during the project will be computer records of events, if they are not continuously overwritten by subsequent revisions.

5.63   The accuracy of the computer system will depend upon the electronic safeguards against subsequent amendments of records and the crosschecks to prevent inaccurate entries.

5.64   Whether or not the system can be accepted as an accurate record, will depend upon whether those inputting data are under a duty to record all information or whether the input is haphazard and infrequent.   If there is a duty to record, then the absence of a record of an event on a particular date may allow an accurate inference that the event did not take place on that date.

5.65   The records of resources used on particular activities and sub-activities are rarely available.   Labour allocation sheets may record manhours and the location of the work, but frequently are insufficiently detailed for productivity analysis without extensive investigation.   If the record of resources is not in the same allocation as the planned resources, then direct comparison may not be possible.

5.66   A plan will usually attempt to level resources using durations and timing to ensure continuity of work for the same level of resource.   If the timing of activities is affected the demand for resource may increase or "stack" over a particular duration.   If the durations are to be maintained then temporary increase in resources is required. Alternatively, if the same level of resource is maintained, then either the start of a activity will be postponed until the resource completes work on other activities, or the duration of the related activities may be prolonged. This level of sophisticated analysis will not be possible without accurate records allocating resources.

5.67   Added to all the above possible inaccuracies, the actual completion of an activity may not be easily identified. In practice, effort on an activity naturally tails off, so that items of work may be left incomplete to be dealt with as part of a snagging list.   The date for completion selected by the expert will then depend on the purpose for which that date is chosen.   If it is selected to demonstrate the possible start of a follow-on activity, the date may differ depending on the activity.

CHAPTER 6 - METHODS OF DELAY ANALYSIS

6.1. THE COMPARISON METHOD

The Comparison Methodology

6.1   The comparison method is fundamental to any delay analysis. Two situations are compared and inferences made both from the differences and from the similarities. The usual comparison is between the past or "actual" situation in which a particular event occurred and a hypothetical situation in which the event did not take place. The comparison identifies both the differences in timing of activities or the difference in distribution of resources and also importantly where there has been no change. The inference is made that the differences can be attributed to the particular event and that where there has been no change that the event has had no effect on that particular characteristic of the project. The method may also be used to compare two hypothetical situations such as the predicted progress of the project with and without the particular event.

6.2   The comparison method is routinely used in the management of projects. This use is relevant to delay analysis because it informs and explains many of the decisions made. Comparison of actual progress at that time to the planned progress is used to monitor the project and may be no more than the comparison of the timing and duration of activities. The method is then used to decide whether and to what extent corrective measures need to be taken in order to bring back activities to the original planned programme.

6.3   It is usual practice when monitoring progress by this method to use a "Rate of Progress TimeLine". In this type of monitoring, the TimeLine for the particular date of assessment is adjusted at each activity on the planned programme to show the percentage completion of each activity. The Line then shows whether or not the activity is on time to the planned programme and the approximate time remaining for each activity. The method has little analytical value for predictions of completion but is useful for identifying trends in progress if a series of TimeLines are compared. The method has little analytical value if actual progress differs substantially from the plan. It is however part of the evidential landscape.

6.4   There are significant limits to this method of monitoring. Some activities may take longer than planned and others less for no other reason than the inaccuracy of the estimated duration. Some risk events predicted in the model represented by the planned programme may not materialise or may not have the effect anticipated. The comparison of actual to planned progress will be a reasonable indication of progress, but only if the construction logic of the programme is actually adopted. Caution is required because a programme is only one model of how the work can be carried out. Actual progress may be different for a number of reasons, not least that risk events may or may not occur, performance may improve at a later stage in the duration of an activity or the method of working may be changed requiring greater initial preparation followed by rapid progress.

6.5   The method may also be used comparing the past and current critical path analysis of the projects. The float trend of individual activities can then be determined and corrective actions taken before the activities become critical or near critical, so maintaining the selected critical path.

The Comparison Method in Delay Analysis

6.6   The comparison method is often used in the various stages of delay analysis.

    6.6.1   A comparison of planned and actual progress of the whole project identifies whether the project proceeded as planned and if not the nature of the change that occurred. The assumption is that if there has been a significant change then the organisation and progress of the project is likely to have been affected by events that are required to be identified and investigated.

    6.6.2   A comparison of planned and actual progress of an activity identifies whether the timing and duration of the activity proceeded as anticipated. The method is used to eliminate those activities of the project from the initial detailed investigation. Again the assumption is that if there is a difference then it is likely that a particular event occurred which affected progress and that the investigation should concentrate on identifying that event.

    6.6.3   The basis of the above assumptions, which may not be correct, is that effort will usually have been directed to achieving and maintaining the planned progress and sequence of activities. The inference is that the effect of an event will have a continuing effect and delay not only the immediate activity but also the planned progress of subsequent activities.

    6.6.4   The comparison method does not deal adequately with the situation where actual progress would have improved on the plan, but has been adversely affected by a particular event. It does not deal adequately with possible deficiencies in the plan.

6.7   The method is also used to compare the planned and actual distribution of resources to identify changes in productivity and efficiency. Used in this way, the method identifies the effect of mitigation measures that reduce or avoid delay by redistribution of existing resources and the introduction of additional resources. The method also allows the identification of the effects of delay on activities which are not on the critical path but which nonetheless result in additional costs through additional resources.

6.8   The accuracy of any inference from the comparison method depends upon the reliability and accuracy of the model of the two situations. The inference from a comparison of a single activity may be relatively accurate particularly if the activity is a milestone or comprises a simple activity of continuous duration. There is less certainty when the activity comprises many non-continuous activities with different resources. The comparison method has little analytical value when used to make inferences as to the cause of delay to completion of the whole project. The inference cannot logically be made that one particular event from all the variables caused the overall delay without more.

6.9   The representation of a project by precise bars on a programme misrepresents the accuracy of the model. As described above, both planned and as-built data may be inaccurate because of the uncertainty of data, which is not evident in the presentation.

6.10   Any inference made by a comparison cannot be certain unless the inference itself is sufficiently probable and is not rebutted by other evidence. It is often the case that many delay analysis are based on small differences between planned and as-built programmes, which can be explained by the inaccuracy of the data.

6.11   The total damage derived using the comparative method may arise from the inaccuracy of the plan as follows:

6.11.1   Part of the delay may be due to inaccuracies in the timing of the activities, or the durations of the activities may be unrealistic and an underestimate.

6.11.2   The price to be paid for the work may be low and less than actual cost of carrying out the planned work.

6.11.3   The risk contingencies of time and/or cost may be insufficient for the risk events that actually occurred.

6.12   An example is given below in Figure 14. This is used to demonstrate the use and limits of the comparison method, on the assumption that the models of the two situations are accurate.

Figure 14 – Comparison – Planned v Actual

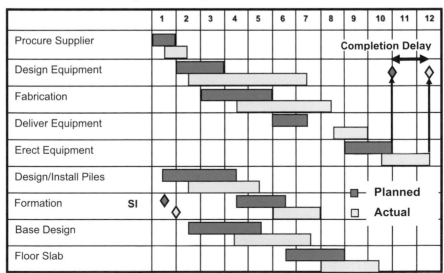

6.13   The example shows that there has been an overall delay to planned completion of the project. The change in the timing and duration of the activities are not in any discernable pattern and does not allow the assumption to be made that the planned construction logic was actually followed. The method does not allow a sufficiently detailed analysis and additional evidence would be required.

6.14   The method identifies two types of changes in the example.

      6.14.1   Changes in the timing or planned commencement of each activity, and

      6.14.2   Changes in planned duration of each activity.

6.15   The analysis of the example is shown more clearly below in Figure 15. The delays to each activity are represented as bars together with the planned duration of the activity. The delay in timing or commencement of the activity is shown first, followed by the planned duration and then followed by the additional duration or prolongation to that planned.

Figure 15 - Example - Delays to Planned Programme

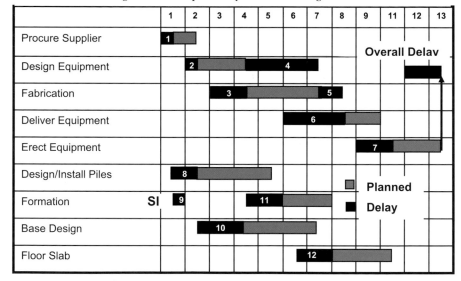

6.16   Some of the timing delays are the same, but it is a logical fallacy to infer from that fact alone that those delays were caused by the same causative event. Indeed the fact that the timing delays are not the same for all activities suggests that there is more than one causative event that has contributed to the overall delay. In addition, the overall delay cannot be calculated by the addition of all the individual activity delays leading to the conclusion that the consequences of the causative events require a more sophisticated analysis than the comparison method.

6.17   The Delay 1 is different to other delays since it is a delay to the first planned activity. The Delay 9 is also different since it is a delay to a milestone. In both cases, it is likely that an investigation of the activity and the milestone will identify the causative event, without investigation of other activities.

6.18 Delays 4 and 5 are also different to other delays, since they are prolongation of the planned duration rather than a delayed commencement. In this case, it may be necessary to investigate other activities and it will be necessary to investigate the work content of the activity and the method of working to identify any change from the plan.

6.19 All other delays will require investigation of the relationship of the activity with others. The comparative method does not however provide a mechanism to do so.

6.20 When the method is used to compare planned and as-built resources, it allows identification of those activities that have involved different resources than planned. The method identifies three types of changes

6.20.1 Changes in level of resources for the planned activity duration, and

6.20.2 Changes in period of planned level of resources, and

6.20.3 Changes in the planned type of resources.

6.21 The first three activities in the example in Figure 15, Delays 1 -5, are shown below in Figure 16 together with the planned and actual resources. The planned resources are shown over the planned duration, but with a time lapse to allow for the delayed start. This allows the planned and actual resource profile for each activity to be compared. Although not shown in the example, it is possible for resources to be allocated to an activity in anticipation of the planned start, so that because of the delay the actual resource profile may commence before actual start of the activity.

Figure 16 - Example – Comparison of Resources – Planned v Actual

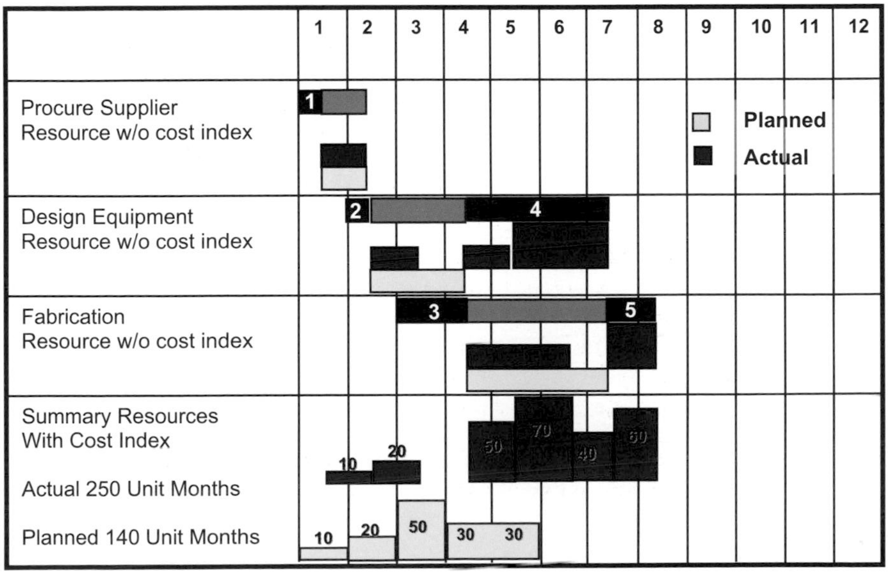

6.22   Delay 1: Although there is a delayed commencement of the first activity "Procure Supplier", Delay 1, the resource data shows that there was no apparent effect on the planned resources. The planned and actual resource profiles are the same. The inference that can be made from all the data is that the cause of Delay 1 did not affect the work content or productivity of the activity such as to require further investigation.

6.23   Delays 2 and 4: The resource data shows that actual resources for activity "Design Equipment" commenced at the planned level, but that part through the planned duration there were no resources allocated to the activity. In the period of Delay 4, resources commenced at the planned level but subsequently increased for the main part of Delay 4. The overall level of resources was greater than planned. This data identifies the key areas of investigation. The period of no activity requires investigation. The substantial increase in resources suggests an increase in work content. The resource profile suggests that efficiency and productivity may need to be investigated to determine the true reasons for the rate of progress.

6.24   Delays 3 and 5: The resource data shows that actual resources for activity "Fabrication" commenced at the planned level, but at the end of planned duration, no resources were allocated to the activity. In the whole period of Delay 5, increased resources were allocated to the activity. The overall level of resources was greater than planned. Again, this data identifies the key areas of investigation. The period of no activity requires investigation, particularly being towards the end of the planned activity duration. The substantial increase in resources suggests an increase in work content. The resource profile suggests not only that efficiency and productivity may need to be investigated but possible acceleration in the period of Delay 5.

6.25   Overall Resources: Figure 16 shows the real time summary of resources based on the unit cost in Figure 13. The difference in the total resources identifies the scale of the changes.

6.26   As demonstrated by the example above, as an initial analysis the comparison method is useful in identifying the first indicators of the areas of investigation required to determine the causes of change. Other than that and in the unique situation of a global claim described below, the comparison method has little analytical value in delay analysis.

Use of Comparison Method in Global, Total Cost & Composite Claims

6.27   The term "Global Claim" is used to describe the use of the comparison method for the whole project or a significant part, without further analysis of the causative connection between the group of events relied on and the extra cost claimed.

6.28   The terms commonly used are defined below, but there is no universal and consistent use of the terms.

   6.28.1   The term "Global Claim" is a general description of a claim for a single sum for more than one separate event, in which there is no breakdown of the contribution of each event to the single sum. The single sum is claimed as the measure of damages or contractual compensation.

6.28.2   The term "Total Cost Claim" is a claim where a single sum is claimed which is the difference between the total actual cost and the contract price or valuation of the work. If the Total Claim is for more than one event, then it is a particular form of a Global Claim.

6.28.3   The terms "Composite Claim" and "Rolled-Up Claim" are claims where there are a number of events and only some are presented as a group in a Global Claim. In this type of claim, separate sums are claimed for particular events and a single sum is claimed for the remaining group of events that are not so particularised. The term "modified Total Cost Claim" is sometimes used to describe this type of claim. Again, this type of claim is a particular type of global claim.

6.29   The global element of a Global Claim is not the events, which generally will be identified, but the alleged extra cost that is claimed to have been caused by the group of events.

6.30   The evaluation of extra cost in the Global Claim is usually based on a comparison between a baseline and the actual cost incurred for the work in issue. The baseline may be the contract price or valuation for the work, or the cost estimated at tender or an estimate of the cost of work had it been unaffected by the events in issue.

6.31   The comparison method of analysis in the form of a global claim is appropriate only in very restricted situations when the particular circumstances justify the approach. Many of the decided cases are concerned solely with the issue whether a claim presented as a Global Claim should be allowed to proceed to trial. The cases show that Global Claims are to be treated with caution and that the adoption of the Global Claim approach does not remove the obligation of the claimant to prove the facts and conditions essential for the inference that the group of events and only the group of events materially caused the extra cost.

6.32   These essential conditions are set out below adopting a structure based on the principles in the Principled Approach which decided cases show apply equally to Global Claims, although not stated in such terms. The conditions in summary are:

6.32.1   Causation. The Initial Condition is that sufficient evidence must be adduced for the inference that extra cost has been incurred due to the group of alleged events.

6.32.2   Proof of Impracticality or Impossibility. It must be proved that it is impracticable or impossible to assess the extra cost due to any of the events in the group in isolation. It must be proved that that there has been an extremely complex interaction between the consequences of the various events in the group, and that as a result it is either difficult or impossible to accurately apportionment the total extra cost between the various events.

6.32.3   The Claimant did not Create the Difficulty. The claim may be defeated if it is shown that any difficulty in assessing the extra cost due to any of the events in the group in isolation was only be caused by the Claimant particularly in delaying making the claim or not keeping the records required by the contract.

6.32.4 <u>Adequate Specification of Events</u>. The listed events in a group must be sufficiently detailed to allow the defendant to know the case it is required to answer. The details must include the description and identification of the events, the defendant's responsibility for each of the events, the fact of the defendant's involvement in causing the alleged global loss, and the method of computation of the loss.

6.32.5 <u>All Events the Responsibility of the Defendant</u>. The listed events described in the group must all be events for which the defendant can have responsibility. The global claim will fail if any material contribution to causation is by events for which the defendant has no responsibility.

6.32.6 <u>Pre-Conditions of Events Satisfied</u>. The contractual pre-conditions for entitlement such as notices must have been satisfied and satisfied in respect of each of the causative events relied upon.

6.32.7 <u>Accurate Representation of Cost</u>. A Global Claim presented as a Total Loss Claim needs to show that it is an accurate representation of the extra cost caused by the events in the group. The extra cost claimed must omit costs due to the claimant's own inefficiencies, or due to the inadequacy of its resources or due to defects caused by the claimant or due to risks for which the claimant is responsible.

Initial Condition

6.33 In a Global Claim, no attempt is made to establish the causal connection between an individual event and the delay and resulting cost. Instead, the basis of the claim is simply that the claimant is entitled to compensation for all and any events in the group of events that may have caused extra cost. The comparison method is used to establish the extra cost.

6.34 If unusually no attempt is made to identify any causative events, then the global claim will fail since there is no legal basis for the claim and no issue of causation arises. It is not enough for the claimant to simply make a global claim in the hope that at some later stage of the proceedings it may be able to prove its case. There must be sufficient detail of the material causes for the Global Claim to proceed.

6.34.1 In *Wharf Properties Ltd v Eric Cumine Associates (No 2)* [1991] 52 BLR 1 Lord Oliver held that even in a Global Claim and a composite claim, the claimant still had to plead its case with sufficient detail to alert the defendant of the case which is going to be made against him at the trial. A claimant could not assert that it was impossible formulate its claim and to continue unspecified in the hope that it could later reconstitute its case and make good the deficiency later.

6.34.2 In *Bernhard's Rugby landscapes Ltd v Stockley Park Consortium Ltd* [1997] 82BLR 39 HH Lloyd J held that whilst a claimant was entitled to present its claim as it considered fit, a defendant was entitled to know the case which it had to meet. As a condition of obtaining leave to amend, Lloyd J ordered the claimant to provide a list that set out in relation to all the alleged causes of delay the relevant contract condition relied upon or any other special circumstance. He also ordered that the nature of the cause or breach must also be detailed. Lloyd J observed that if the claimant's case was not properly pleaded and the defendant was embarrassed, then the claim might be struck out.

6.34.3   If for instance one of the events is that the specification of particular equipment was inadequate, then sufficient details would include how the specification was inadequate and the effect on a particular inadequacy to a particular trade or why the inadequacy contributed to the delay and extra cost and the dates between which the delay occurred and whether such delay was continuous or intermittent. Similarly, if the event was delay due to supply of information it is necessary to give details when the information ought to have been given, when it was given or the nature of the work which was delayed or why it was delayed *Imperial Chemical Industries -v- Bovis Construction Ltd and Others* (1992) 32 CON LR 90.

6.34.4   The claimant must give an adequate specification of the events. Allowing a Global Claim to proceed did not give the claimant carte blanche to attempt to prove the extra cost in any way they chose. The claimant's pleadings remained the measure of what the claimant was entitled to prove by way of computation of extra cost. If a lesser claim was to be made out, that was to be done on the basis of evidence properly led within the scope of the existing pleadings *John Doyle Construction Limited v Laing Management (Scotland) Limited* [2004] 1BLR 295 Inner House

6.35   If the causative events are identified, the basis of the global claim is that causation is inferred rather than demonstrated[27]. The logic of the global claim is based on the inference from the coincidence of three facts that the group of events caused the overall extra cost.

6.35.1   Each of the events in the group of events is capable of causing extra cost.

6.35.2   Each of the events in the group is likely on the facts to have caused some extra cost.

6.35.3   There has been overall extra cost.

6.36   If it is shown that one of the events in the group could not have caused the extra cost, that is not necessarily fatal to the global claim, but simply reduces the number of causative events. In *J. Crosby and Sons Ltd v Portland Urban and District Council* [1977] 5 BLR 121, Donaldson J held that if the arbitrator had inadvertently included in the group of events causing a complex of delays and disorganisation, an event which caused neither delay nor disorganisation it did not matter greatly because the arbitrator had not thereby enlarged his assessment of the additional expense which formed the

---

[27]   Byrne J of the Supreme Court of Victoria in *John Holland Construction & Engineering Pty Ltd v Kvaerner RJ Brown Pty Ltd*, [1996]82BLR83 approved in *John Doyle Construction Limited v Laing Management (Scotland) Limited* [2004] 1BLR 295.

basis of his award.

6.37   The above three facts are evidence of neither the entitlement nor of the extra cost caused by the group of events, if any. It follows that if there are other explanations for the extra cost which are events which are not the responsibility of the defendant then the strength of the inference which is the basis of the global claim will be reduced.

6.38   In some cases, the quantum of extra costs may be explained by the inaccuracies in the comparative method.

6.38.1   If the baseline for the analysis is either the planned programme or the planned allocation of resources they must be accurate otherwise logically the global claim analysis is flawed. In that case, part of the delay or additional cost will be inherent in the plan and not a consequence of the group of events. The inadequacy in the tender in terms of price, programme and resources may be the cause of some of the extra cost claimed.

6.38.2   Further, if the actual delay or additional cost was incurred unreasonably by for instance the claimant's failure to comply with any obligations of mitigation, then again logically the global claim analysis is flawed. In that case, part of the delay or extra cost will be caused by the failure of the claimant and not a consequence of the group of events.

6.39   The extent of the inaccuracy of the comparison method may be sufficient to rebut any inference that the alleged group of events could have caused any of the extra cost claimed. In that case, the issue of causation does not arise and the global claim will fail.

6.40   The above principles are consistent with the principle in the Principled Approach when applied to a global claim that if the group of events could not have affected the damage related to the particular obligation in issue, then the matter of causation does not arise.

Fairness, Value Judgment and Commonsense

6.41   The difficulty which the Global Claim is intended to address, is that events in the group may inter-react with each other in a complex way, so that it becomes difficult, if not impossible, to identify what extra cost each event has caused. There are three tensions at work whenever the Global Claim jurisprudence is relied on:

6.41.1   The Global Claim may be the only practical way to prevent the defendant benefiting from the situation of a highly complicated project created by the defendant or by events for which the defendant is solely responsible or at his risk. In that case, the difficulty of establishing the individual nexus of events should not prevent the claimant succeeding.

6.41.2   The Global Claim approach may be used because the claim lacks merit and that if the proper nexus was demonstrated it would show the claim to be a bogus claim or a grossly inflated claim. In that case, the requirement for the usual investigation of causal nexus will expose the nature of the claim.

6.41.3   As a matter of fairness and in observance of the principles of natural justice the defendant should be provided with sufficient detail of the nexus of the causal effect of an interaction of events in an intelligible form so that the defendant knows exactly the case it is required to meet *John Holland Construction & Engineering Pty Ltd v Kvaerner RJ Brown Pty Ltd*, [1996]82BLR83.

6.42   In a Global Claim, it is not the events that are difficult to assess, but the nexus with the extra cost that is impracticable or impossible to ascertain with any detail. The jurisprudence of the Global Claim allows the extra cost based on the comparative method to be the prima facie measure of damage, but only if the claimant proves the facts and conditions essential for the inference that the group of events and only the group of events materially caused the extra cost.

6.43   Even though it is unattractive that the defendant that created the difficulty should benefit from the situation, nonetheless the evidential burden upon the claimant to adequately prove its case still remains even in a Global Claim *Skanska Construction UK Ltd v Eggar (Barony) Ltd* [2004] EWHC 1748 .

6.44   As described above, in a Global Claim each of the events in the group events alleged to have caused the extra cost must be adequately specified by the claimant *John Doyle Construction Limited v Laing Management (Scotland) Limited* [2004] 1BLR 295 Inner House.

6.45   The concept of the Global Claim was approved by Donaldson J (as he then was) in *J. Crosby and Sons Ltd v Portland Urban and District Council* [1977] 5 BLR 121. In that case, the Global Claim was in the form of a composite claim. Donaldson J accepted a composite claim but on the basis of the findings of fact by the arbitrator that it was impracticable, if not impossible, to assess the additional cost caused by delay and disorganization due to any one of the matters in a group in isolation from the other matters.

6.46   The important first condition, which must be proved by the claimant in a Global Claim, is that it is impracticable or impossible to assess the extra cost due to any of the events in the group in isolation. It must be proved that it is impossible or impractical to disentangle the events and the consequences. It must be proved

6.46.1   that there has been an extremely complex interaction between the consequences of the various events in the group, and

6.46.2   that as a result it was either difficult or impossible to accurately apportionment the total extra cost between the various events.

6.47   In some straightforward cases, the aspect of the nexus will be apparent from the nature of the event and the loss alleged. In that case, all that will be necessary is a statement of the facts giving rise to the causal nexus and if necessary with details. It will rare in construction contracts that this first condition will be capable of being proved for a large group of events, simply by reference to the nature of the events themselves. In most cases, the causal connection must be fully set out. It is necessary to prove how the events interact and why the alleged consequences on extra cost cannot in practice be identified. Many standard forms have detailed provisions for the keeping of records at the time the events occur so that it is possible at the time to identify precisely those events which may interact and the extent to which they do. The effect of such records will lead to possible composite claims but of reduced scope.

6.48 In *London Borough of Merton v Stanley Hugh Leach* [1985] 32 BLR 51 Vinelott J dealt with an appeal from an arbitrator's decisions on preliminary issues. In accepting that a global claim could be made it was assumed for the purpose of the preliminary issue only, that the condition of impracticality was satisfied. Vinelott J then identified a further condition that needed to be satisfied if ascertainment by a Global Claim was to be allowed. The second condition is that the claimant should not unreasonably have delayed in making the claim and so himself have created the difficulty.

6.49 In *John Doyle Construction Limited v Laing Management (Scotland) Limited* [2004] 1BLR 295 Inner House further conditions were identified which had to be satisfied to permit a claim to be advanced as a Global Claim. The third condition is that the Claimant must give an adequate specification of:

6.49.1 the events,

6.49.2 the defendant's responsibility for each of the events,

6.49.3 the fact of the defendant's involvement in causing the alleged global loss, and

6.49.4 the method of computation of the loss.

6.50 Even if the Global Claim fails because the above conditions cannot be proved, that does not mean that no claim will succeed. After evidence has been adduced, there may be a sufficient basis to find causal connections between some individual losses and individual events, or to make a rational apportionment of part of the global loss to the causative events for which the defendant has been held responsible. That possibility is one of the reasons why some Global Claims will be allowed to proceed to trial. Nonetheless the claimant advancing a Global Claim takes a risk since if it fails there may not be any rational basis for the award of a lesser sum *John Doyle Construction Limited v Laing Management (Scotland) Limited* [2004] 1BLR 295 Inner House.

6.51 In *London Underground Limited v Citylink Telecommunications Ltd* [2007] EWHC 1749 (TCC) Ramsey J considered the approach to be adopted in dealing with a claim that survived the failure of a global claim.

6.51.1 Ramsey J observed that the surviving or remaining claim would emerge from the evidence that had been adduced to establish or deal with the global claim. There would clearly be a need for analysis of the existing evidence to see if there was a sufficient basis for establishing causation.

6.51.2 Ramsey J observed that where the case had proceeded on the basis of a global claim, it would be at the stage when the tribunal had determined what events could be relied upon that it would be possible to carry out the analysis of any surviving claim. Necessarily in such a case, as in many cases where there was partial success, neither party would have a specific opportunity to deal with a case based on the tribunal's particular findings. Tribunals frequently had to deal with cases where a claim or a defence had not wholly succeeded and it was necessary to determine what result flows from the partial success or failure.

6.51.3   Ramsey J held that provided that the result was based on primary facts which had been in issue in the proceedings, there was in principle no objection to a tribunal taking such a course. There were limits and it was be a matter of fact or degree in a particular case whether the findings made by the Arbitrator fell outside the limits and whether fairness required the Arbitrator to seek further submissions from the parties.

6.52   A claimant cannot assume the Tribunal will make its case if the global claim fails. The Tribunal is required to consider the evidence available and if it considers that the surviving claim is implicit in the case and that it may need to be considered, it must decide whether or not to seek further submissions. In most cases, the Tribunal will not proceed immediately to deciding the surviving claim but will give the parties the opportunity to make further submissions.

6.53   The principles set out above are consistent with the principle in the Principled Approach applied to global claims that a value judgment is required of the particular obligation in issue. The judgment is whether or not it is fair that the party in breach of the obligation should make at least some contribution for the indivisible damage and where appropriate in proportion to the material contribution to the change in risk caused by the parties.

Entitlement to Compensation and Allocation of Risk

6.54   The alleged difficulties that give rise to the Global Claim do not absolve the claimant from proving the causal connections between the events and the extra cost. If the essential conditions for a Global Claim are proved, then the claimant is not required to prove the extra cost caused by each separate event. There is no need to prove the contribution of each event in the group to the overall extra cost, only that each event had some contribution.

6.55   In *John Holland Construction & Engineering Pty Ltd v Kvaerner RJ Brown Pty Ltd*, [1996]82BLR83 , Byrne J stated that the logic of a Global Claim is that given that the breaches of contract caused some extra cost, they must have caused the whole of the extra cost because no other relevant cause was responsible for any part of it.

6.56   The legal basis for allowing the Global Claim is that the defendant's breaches, or events which are the defendant's risk, are the only causally significant factors for all the delay or additional cost claimed. The logic is that since all the causative events are the responsibility of the defendant, there is no need to demonstrate a causative link between each event and the claimed consequences of extra cost.

6.57   It is this logic that leads, in addition to the three conditions identified above, to a fourth essential condition of the Global Claim that all of the events that caused the alleged extra cost must be the responsibility of the defendant. If it is proved that part of the loss was caused by events that are not the responsibility of the defendant then the claim will fail.

6.58   If the events which caused the extra cost include events for which the defendant has no liability, then the effect of upholding a global claim would be to impose on the defendant a liability which was not, at least in part, legally his. That is unjustified - HH Judge Wilcox in *Skanska Construction UK Ltd v Eggar (Barony) Ltd* [2004] EWHC 1748 .

6.59   In practice, the claimant may not list all the matters that may have contributed to the alleged extra cost and particularly his own inefficiencies. The defendant therefore has a choice. He may simply put the claimant to proof that the each of the events in the group was one for which the defendant was responsible. The defender may in addition set out to prove that a material contribution to the causation of the global loss has been made by additional factors for which he has no liability. If he succeeds in proving that, the global claim will be undermined *John Doyle Construction Limited v Laing Management (Scotland) Limited* [2004] 1BLR 295 Inner House.

6.60   The assessment of the extra cost must not include types of cost for which the defendant is not liable, since that also will be unjustified. This may be particularly significant if the events in the group require different methods of assessment under the contract.

6.61   In *J. Crosby and Sons Ltd v Portland Urban and District Council* [1977] 5 BLR 121 the arbitrator only awarded on a global basis where all the events were solely the responsibility of the defendant and for which there was a monetary entitlement. Donaldson J accepted that the arbitrator could make individual awards in respect of those parts of individual items of claim that could be dealt with in isolation and a supplementary award in respect of the remainder of these claims as a composite whole. The provisos were that there was no duplication and there was no profit in the award, since the entitlement for some of the matters fell to be valued under clauses that allowed profit and some under clauses that did not. This approach was consistent with the risk allocation under the contract for some of the events. This approach was also followed by Vinelott J in *London Borough of Merton v Stanley Hugh Leach,* [1985] 32 BLR 51**.**

6.62   In many forms of contract, the defendant will not have responsibility for an event unless the contractual preconditions of entitlement have been satisfied. It is therefore necessary for the contract preconditions to be satisfied for each event in the group, otherwise awarding on the basis of the Global Claim will be contrary to the contract allocation of risk and again not justified.

6.63   In *London Borough of Merton v Stanley Hugh Leach,* [1985] 32 BLR 51 Vinelott J emphasised that apart from proving practical impossibility, a rolled up award could only be made where the conditions which had to be satisfied before an award could be made had been satisfied in relation to each head of claim. In order for the claimant to be entitled to extra cost as a global claim any pre-conditions which are made applicable to such claims by the terms of the relevant contract had to be satisfied, and satisfied in respect of each of the causative events relied upon *Mid Glamorgan County Council v J. Devonald Williams and Partners* [1992] 29CONLR129..

6.64   In addition to the restrictions described above, a Global Claim presented as a Total Loss Claim needs to show that it is an accurate representation of the extra cost caused by the events in the group. Such a claim is unlikely to succeed.

6.65   The case of *London Borough of Merton v Stanley Hugh Leach* [1985] 32 BLR 51 was an appeal from an arbitrator's decisions on preliminary issues. Issue 13 was whether there could be recovery of a global loss based on a calculation of total loss. In this case, the calculation was based on the contractor's direct site costs to which was added profit and overheads and then compared with the tender figure.

   6.65.1   Vinelott J. held that the calculation was not even an approximation for a claim whether rolled up or under the contract clauses. He considered that the approach relieved the contractor from any burden of additional costs resulting from delays for which the contractor was not entitled to any extension of time at all.

   6.65.2   Vinelott J. held that such a calculation might be appropriate for a *quantum meruit* or for a partial *quantum meruit* to reflect additional expense that could not be calculated in accordance with contract machinery because of a default by Merton. In this case, that was not a claim that Leach was entitled to pursue.

   6.65.3   The arbitrator identified the fundamental assumption of a Total Loss Claim which undermines its accuracy. The Total Loss Claim in that case compared a building contract which proceeded to completion without any hitch, delay or variation whatsoever with the tender figure. However that ideal situation is rarely, if ever, met and he found was not met in the instant contract. Accordingly, the sums in the Total Cost Claim included the costs to the claimant of all the 'hitches' of whatever nature that occurred on the site.

6.66   In *Petromec Inc v Petroleo Brasileiro SA* [2007] EWHC 1589 the issue was the assessment of the amount due for the changes in specification.

   6.66.1   The contract prescribed a reasonable extra cost to be determined. Petromec's assessment was the difference between the total actual cost and the alleged projected cost to the original specification, instead of the valuation of each variation.

   6.66.2   Mr Justice Cooke held that Petromec's methodology assumed that which had to be proved and attempted to reverse the burden of proof. He held that the causal nexus between each instruction and the extra cost had to be proved.

   6.66.3   It was held that it made no difference whether consideration was being given to multiple breaches or multiple variations. The overall principle remained the same. There was a need to show the consequences of complying with the instruction in terms of work done and cost reasonably incurred. The causal nexus was important and had to be spelt out in an intelligible form. The line of authorities of *Bernhard's Rugby landscapes Ltd v Stockley Park Consortium Ltd* [1997] 82BLR 39, *Wharf Properties Ltd v Eric Cumine Associates (No 2)* [1991] 52 BLR 1 and *John Holland Construction & Engineering Pty Ltd v Kvaerner RJ Brown Pty Ltd*, [1996]82BLR83 were of direct application.

6.66.4 It was held that if Petromec's methodology had been sufficient to prove its case, it would not have been debarred from pleading and proving it by that method, but its methodology was not what the contract envisaged, was not what the law allowed and was not what the Rules of Court required for it to put and establish its case.

6.67 The principles set out above are consistent with the principle in the Principled Approach applied to global claims that evidence must be adduced to allow the inference to be made that the group of events occurred and that they were each a breach of a legal obligation which entitles compensation for the damage. They are also consistent with the further requirement that the contract allocation of risk is given effect by preventing any allocation of liability for the global claim which would upset that risk allocation.

Limits on Use of Comparison Method

6.68 The comparison method is useful to show graphically the progress of the works, but it has little analytical value particularly when there are multiple causative events and disputes as to the responsibility for those causes. It does not allow analysis of causation and the effect of one causative event on the progress of subsequent activities.

6.69 The limitation of the method in practice is demonstrated in *McAlpine Humberoak Ltd v McDermott International Inc.* [1992] 58BLR1 CA. McAlpine was sub-contractor to McDermott and alleged that the main cause of delay was the issue of a large number of revised drawings, the failure of McDermott to answer technical queries (TQ's) promptly and the issue of variation orders (VO's).

6.69.1 McAlpine's methodology involved the preparation of charts to demonstrate the cumulative effect of all causes of delay including drawing revisions, TQ's and VO's. It was held that the flaw was the assumption that if one man was working for one day on a particular VO, the whole contract was held up for that day. The method was defective because it assumed that the whole of the workforce planned for a particular activity was engaged continuously in that activity from the day it started until the day it finished. That was hardly likely to be so.

6.69.2 It was held that the defects in the methodology meant that McAlpine did not come near to proving that the delay in delivery and indirect costs was due to the revised drawings, VO's and late response to TQ's. Although the total cost was claimed as £3,548,848 this was nearly £1m more than the McAlpine's actual costs. This was considered significant.

6.70 The correct approach on the matter of causation approved in *McAlpine Humberoak Ltd v McDermott International Inc.* [1992] 58BLR1 CA was a retrospective and dissectional reconstruction by expert evidence of events almost day by day, drawings by drawing, TQ by TQ and weld procedure by weld procedure to show the effect of the issue of drawings and whether or not they really had any retarding or disruptive effect on progress.

6.2. THE LOGIC LINKED PROGRAMME

Network Programmes

6.71   An important fourth dimension of a project is the construction logic that defines the conditions for work to commence, proceed and be completed.

6.72   The construction logic represents those factors which define the construction sequence of the project and include:

6.72.1   *the method of working*, showing how the project is to be carried out and the sequence of activities;

6.72.2   *the construction constraints*, which may be access dates for parts of the site or release dates for information or delivery dates for work by others;

6.72.3   *the resource restraints*, which recognise the limited availability of plant, equipment, labour and supply of materials. The resource restraint is usually modelled by the sequential linking of activities that use the same resource. Experience shows that the resource restraint is often not appreciated when delay analysis is carried out.

6.73   The absence of this fourth dimension from the Bar Chart means that it does not provide an adequate model to analyse the consequences of an event on progress. Without construction logic, the Bar Chart cannot provide the means for measuring the time consequences of events and cannot identify from multiple delays those that had an effect on progress and those that did not.

6.74   The construction logic can be depicted graphically as a Network Programme, which is a useful device to explain the complex inter-relationship between activities and to model dependencies. There are two basic types of network; Activity-on-Arrow and Activity-on-Node.

Activity-on-Arrow

6.75   The term "activity-on-arrow network" is defined in BS 6079-2:2000 as a network in which arrows symbolise the activities[28].

6.76   In the Activity-on-Arrow logic diagram the start and end of an activity is a node. The end node of one activity is the start node of the succeeding activity. The start and end nodes are connected by an arrow. The two nodes and the arrow are together referred to as the activity. The nodes are numbered so that the activity is identified by the start and finish node numbers. The combination of activities is a model of the flow of work.

---

[28]   BS 6079-2:2000 Paragraph 2.6.

6.77   An example is shown below in Figure 15, which is the project shown in the above Bar Chart at Figure 12.

Figure 15 – Activity on Arrow

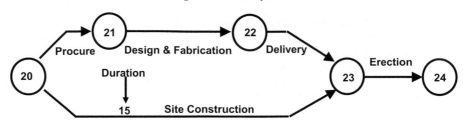

6.78   In the example above, there are four activities which must be completed before erection of the equipment on site can be carried out, three relating to the procurement, design & fabrication and delivery of the equipment and one representing the site construction required to be carried out.

6.79   The activity "Erection" is identified as Activity 23-24. Node 23 represents the start of Activity 23-24, but also the finish of Activities 22-23 and 20-23, which shows that the logic inherent in the Activity-on-Arrow is *finish-to-start*.

6.80   The arrow activity is not drawn to a time-scale but the duration is annotated as shown in the example. The Activity-on-Arrow Network is useful in representing the flow of work and requires a rigorous approach to construction logic.

6.81   In the example above, if the intention is that the equipment is to be delivered directly to its final position on the floor slab without temporary storage at site, then the Activity 20-23 "Site Construction" is insufficiently detailed to allow accurate representation of the project logic. In that case two additional activities are required identifying the floor slab construction and the extended storage at the fabricators.

6.82   This is shown in Figure 16 below.

Figure 16 – Revised Activity on Arrow

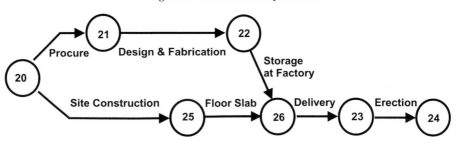

Activity-on-Node

6.83   The term "activity-on-node network is defined in BS 6079-2:2000 as a network in which the nodes symbolise the activities[29].

6.84   In the Activity-on-Node logic diagram, each node represents an activity, rather than part of an activity as in the Activity-on-Arrow logic diagram. The arrows between nodes only represent the relationship or the logic link between the activities. Activity-on-node logic diagrams use only relational arrows that connect the finish of one activity with the start of the subsequent activity, which are *finish to start* relationship links that are the same as used in Activity-on-Arrow logic diagrams.

6.85   An example is shown below in Figure 17.

Figure 17 – Activity on Node

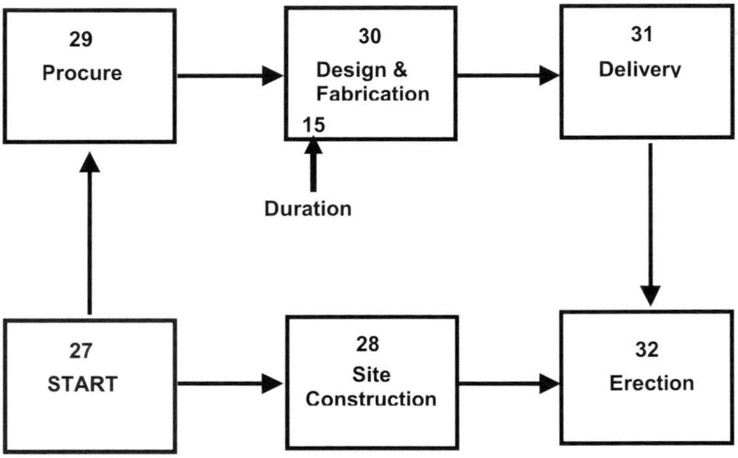

6.86   The Precedence Network Method is now the most common form of Activity-on-Node Programme and uses the possibility of defining the links between activities by relationships other than *finish-to-start*. This method permits not only *finish-to-start* links but also *start-to-finish* links, *start-to-start* links and *finish-to-finish* links. The choice of logic link depends on which link accurately models the particular restraint.

6.87   The Method also allows a time dimension to be added to the link in the form of a *lag* or *lead*. As shown below the *lag* or *lead* is a device to allow the simplicity of presentation to be maintained. If adjustments are not made to the time dimension in the *lag* or *lead* when analysing delay, their use may lead to illogical results and inaccuracies in the analysis.

---

[29]   BS 6079-2:2000 Paragraph 2.7.

Logic Links

6.88   The most significant logic link is the *"Finish-to-Start"*. If the physical construction logic prevent a subsequent activity starting until the preceding activity is finished, then this is a true *"Finish-to-Start"* link that cannot be altered by actual progress. An example is the activity of "Erection" of the equipment in the project above and the preceding activity of "Floor Slab". If erection cannot physically commence until all the floor slab has been constructed, due for instance to the size of the Equipment relative to that of the floor slab, then the *"Finish-to-Start"* link will accurately model the project.

6.89   In practice, the *"Finish-to-Start"* link is used even when the physical construction logic does not demand such a link. Instead, the link may be dictated by management requirements such as available resources and the movement of trades from one activity to the next. In any delay analysis, such logic links will need to be re-examined to establish that they are still accurate in the context of actual facts.

6.90   An example of *"Finish-to-Start"* logic is shown below in Figure 18 for the three activities of procurement, design and fabrication of equipment in the project shown in the Bar Chart in Figure 12 above.

Figure 18 – Logic Links – Start to Finish

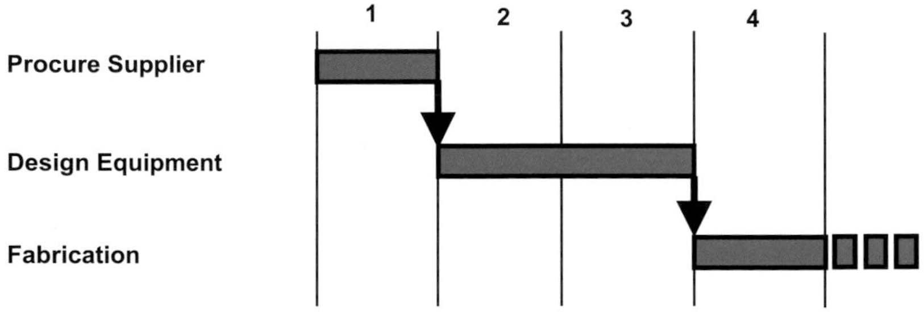

6.91   The construction logic is that the activity "Design Equipment" will not start until the supplier has been procured. If the design by the Supplier will not take place until an order is issued, then the *finish-to-start* logic accurately represents the relationship between these two activities. If however the Employer is involved in earlier design decisions that may affect the completion of procurement or the commencement of design, then additional activities will be required to accurately model the restraints.

6.92   If the fabrication of the equipment is not to start until all the design is completed, then the *finish-to-start* link will accurately describe the relationship between the activities "Design Equipment" and "Fabrication". In practice, although the start of "Fabrication" will depend on the progress of "Design Equipment" it is likely that "Fabrication" can and will commence when part of the preceding activity "Design Equipment" has been carried out, if the pace of design is faster than that of fabrication. Once part of the design is completed, this will allow fabrication to commence. In that case, if the *"Finish-to-Start"* logic link is to be used then an accurate model requires the significant phases of the activities to be represented to properly model the phased construction.

6.93   This is shown in the above example by expanding the description of the activities represented by two sub-activities to model the two linked phases of design and fabrication, in Figure 19 below.

Figure 19 – Expanded Logic Links – Phased Design

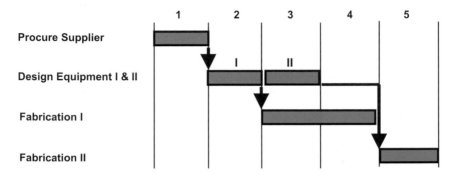

6.94   The expanded logic diagram in Figure 19 above shows that once the first phase of "Design Equipment" is completed, then the first phase of "Fabrication" can commence. The second phase of fabrication requires both the second phase of design and the first phase of fabrication to be completed. The estimated duration of "Fabrication I" is longer than "Design Equipment II" so the expanded model anticipates a delay after completion of "Design II" before start of "Fabrication II". The length of the delay is the difference between the duration of "Fabrication I" and "Design Equipment II".

6.95   The expansion of activities to show their sub-activities can lead to large and complex programmes. Logic links other than *finish-to-start* are used in order to reduce complexity of programmes.

6.96   This is shown below in Figure 20 for the example above. The activities of "Design Equipment" and "Fabrication" are shown as continuous single activities, but with *start-to-start* and *finish-to-finish* logic links and each with a lag. The lag is not an absolute time dimension but is simply a device to simplify presentation that may require adjustment in any delay analysis.

Figure 20 – Start-to-Start & Finish-to-Finish Links – Phased Design

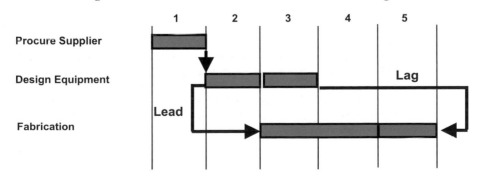

6.97 The *start-to-start* link in Figure 20 has a lead that is calculated as the time required to complete the first phase of "Design Equipment" so as to allow the start of the first phase of "Fabrication". If the commencement of "Design Equipment" is delayed then the *start-to-start* link remains accurate to analyse the effects of delay. If however the activity "Design Equipment" is prolonged, then the lead in the *start-to-start* link will need to be adjusted commensurate with the prolongation of the first phase of "Design Equipment" in order to maintain the accuracy of the model.

6.98 The *finish-to-finish* link in Figure 20 has a lag calculated as the sum of two different periods. The first part of the lag is the difference between the period required for second part of "Design Equipment" and the period for the first part of "Fabrication". If the second part of "Design Equipment" is prolonged, then the lag in the *finish-to-finish* link will need to be adjusted for the change in the difference between the two above periods in order to maintain the accuracy of the model. The second part of the *finish-to-finish* link lag is the period required for the second part of "Fabrication". Again, if that period is prolonged then the lag will need to be adjusted.

6.99 Whilst the introduction of *start-to-start* and *finish-to-finish* logic links with leads and lags simplifies presentation, it also provides an inherent source of potential inaccuracy in any delay analysis. It is often difficult in a complex network programmes to identify the basis of each and every lead and lag and therefore to make the necessary adjustments in the context of actual facts to maintain the accuracy of the model.

Linked Bar Chart

6.100 The introduction of logic links to create the Linked Bar Chart allows the time dimension of the project to be defined by the relationship of activities one to the other. The Bar Chart previously shown is repeated below in Figure 21, as a Linked Bar Chart.

Figure 21 – Linked Bar Chart Programme

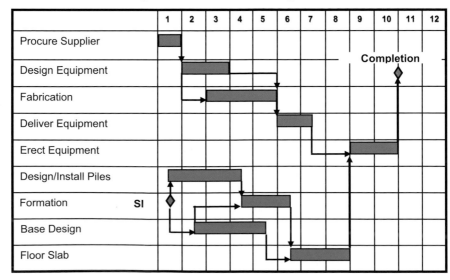

6.101   The example above shows the milestone types of activity "SI" and "Completion". The other activities are shown as continuous bars of effort. The different types of logic link are also shown of *finish-to-start*, *start-to-start* and *finish-to-finish*.

6.102   The Linked Bar Chart is simply a graphic representation. Although it allows an easier understanding of a complex project, the clean lines and the crisp presentation may give a false impression of accuracy. The accuracy of the representation will depend upon the accuracy of the main dimensions as explained in more detail above.

   6.102.1   <u>The Project Activities</u>: The list of activities must be complete if they are accurately to represent the whole Project. Activities that are commonly overlooked are plant and material procurement and delivery, the procedure for submission and approval of drawings particularly shop drawings and the testing of structures or machinery. Activities which do not appear to be initially critical, which appear to be unrelated to other activities and which theoretically can be carried out at any time, are frequently overlooked.

   6.102.2   <u>The Timing of Activities</u>: The accuracy of the start date of the activities depends upon the technical details of the work content together with the design, physical and resource restraints. Irrespective of the details of the Bar Chart, the start date will always involve assumptions that may not be represented by logic links. For instance, it is unusual for the incidence and frequency of loads and capacity resulting from design of one activity not to affect the design of another activity. This relationship is often assumed in fixing the start date, but not demonstrated by any logic link.

   6.102.3   <u>The Duration of Activities</u>: The accuracy of the duration of activities depends upon the level of resources and productivity, the fixed time periods for approvals or for tests and the time risk contingency. The duration of activities are frequently not continuous nor necessarily involves the same resources for the full period. The greater the diversity of the activities comprising the activity the more likely that the activity bar will not comprise continuous effort of the same type of resource. The finish of an activity may be different depending upon the subsequent activity being considered.

   6.102.4   <u>The Logic Links</u>: The logic links must be complete. Frequently cross-links between different parts of the design are not identified because the emphasis is on construction activities. The type of link selected must be accurate. The introduction of lags in *start-to-start* and *finish-to-finish* links in particular may require adjustment in any analysis. The lag is not an absolute time dimension but is simply a device to simplify presentation.

Critical Path Network

6.103   The analysis of the critical path is usually carried out using commercially available software programmes, simply because of the large number of activities.

6.104   The accuracy of the critical path analysis depends upon the accuracy of the main dimensions of the project as described above for the Bar Chart and the Linked Bar Chart.

6.105   An additional source of inaccuracy introduced by the critical path analysis is the algorithm used in the software. Commercial programmes use different algorithms that may not give the same results. The software may contain instructions for the allocation of float or for dealing with concurrency that may lead to inaccuracies.

6.106   The previously shown Linked Bar Chart is shown below in Figure 22 analysed for the critical path.

Figure 22 – Critical Path Network

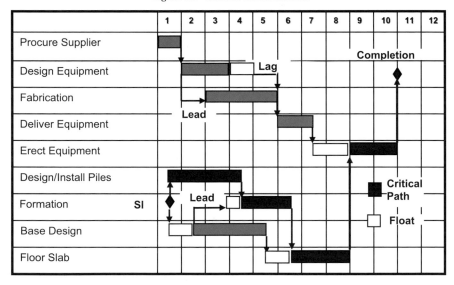

6.107   In the example above the two main characteristics of critical path analysis are shown, the critical path and float. There are various types of float, all of which are an expression of the relationship of an activity to other activities and milestones. The term "float" is defined in BS 6079-1:2000 as the time available for an activity in addition to its planned duration[30]. The term "free float" is defined as the time by which an activity may be delayed or extended without affecting the start date of any

---

[30]   BS 6079-2:2000 Paragraph 2.68.

succeeding activity[31]. The term "total float" is defined as the time by which an activity may be delayed or extended without affecting the total project duration[32].

6.108 The activities with the least total float are on the critical path to completion. Those activities that can be least delayed without affecting the Date for Completion are said to be on the critical path. The line through those activities is the critical path to completion.

6.109 The float in a programme is an important project dimension that allows informed management decisions to be taken but only if the analysis is accurate. A sophisticated approach is to use a "Float Trend Analysis" in which the tendency of activities over time towards becoming critical is monitored and used as a means to decide priority of action. The accurate identification of float and the availability of powerful computers, also allows rapid analysis of the effect of optimization of resources using the special features of commercially available programmes. The approach is to take account of the delays and changes in sequence caused by events and to level the resources over the float periods. The network programme is re-calculated changing the amended duration of activities to accommodate more efficient use and movement of resources. In this way, the time implication of different mitigation measures can be analysed.

6.110 Two types of float are shown in the example above. The first type of float is generated by the analysis and is shown for activities "Deliver Equipment" and "Base Design". The analysis shows the extent to which delivery of equipment might be delayed without affecting "Completion", if other activities maintain schedule. This first type of float is also shown for activity "Base Design" which shows the extent to which the completion of the "Base Design" might be delayed without affecting "Completion".

6.111 In the above example, the site construction involving the installation of piles, construction of Formation and Floor Slab and the erection of the Equipment at site are shown as being critical. If the logic is actually followed, and the start or finish dates for any of these activities are different to programmed, then the completion date will be affected (unless the changes cancel out). If the planned date is to be maintained then priority will need to be given to the critical activities.

6.112 The second type of float shown in the example above is frequently not generated by the programme analysis, but instead is embedded as absolute time in the lead in the *start-to-start* link and the lag in the *finish-to-finish* link. The characteristic functions in the same way as float, but is not usually referred to as float and often overlooked in analysis. In the example above the completion of the second part of "Design Equipment" may take longer than shown on the programme without affecting completion. Provided the second part of "Design Equipment" takes no longer than the first part of "Fabrication" then the progress of "Design Equipment" will not affect subsequent activities. The "Design Equipment" *finish-to-finish* lag itself will need to be adjusted to take into account actual events, if the analysis is to be accurate. A similar type of float is shown for the *start-to-start* lead for "Base Design".

---

[31]   BS 6079-2:2000 Paragraph 2.70.

[32]   BS 6079-2:2000 Paragraph 2.175.

6.3. THE IMPACTED AS-PLANNED METHOD

The Impacted As-Planned Method

6.113   The impact as-planned method uses the planned programme to analyse the effect of causative events on planned progress[33]. The event is first represented as an activity of fixed duration. Often the duration of the activity is the delay or prolongation identified as caused by the event based on a separate or sub-network analysis. The activity is then impacted on the as-planned programme to determine the consequences on planned progress.

6.114   As explained above the appropriate as-planned programme must be adopted which sets out the complete representation of the project. In many projects, the planned programme is developed in the early stages, so that it is only later revisions that provide a complete model for analysis. Often the as-planned programme must be constructed from available information to represent the intention at commencement of the project.

6.115   If the as-planned programme used for analysis is not reliable and achievable then any impact analysis will be flawed. The planned programme is susceptible to all the inaccuracies described above for the critical path network. The original as-planned programme may include durations for activities that include assessment of likely delay as a risk contingency, but the activity itself may be unreasonable for the work involved. That distinction needs to be made on the as-planned programme if the analysis of delay is to be accurate.

The Time Disconformities of the Delay Activity

6.116   It is an inherent part of the impacted as-planned method that the delay activity will not necessarily be shown on the impacted as-planned programme in the time period when the event or delay actually occurred. There may be a time disconformity between the assessment of the delay activity and analysis of its effect. The extent and importance of that discontinuity will depend upon the extent of the lack of correlation between the impacted as-planned programme and the actual construction progress and the nature of the event.

6.117   If the event prevents commencement of an activity at the beginning of a project, such as the lack of access or lack of information, then the duration of the delay event can accurately be assessed by comparison of the date when the activity was planned to start and the date when it could start after access was granted or the information provided. Later in the project, the accuracy of the assessment of the duration of the delay event will depend upon the accuracy of the correlation of the impacted as-planned programme and actual progress.

6.118   The timing of an event in the progress of an activity may be highly relevant to the calculation of the delay caused to the activity. So for instance a variation issued early

---

[33]   The difficulties and reliability of the as-planned programme are examined below at Section 5.3 "The Planned Programme".

in the progress of the activity may have less effect than if issued later when there may be extensive abortive work and re-work. A large discontinuity with actual progress will not allow the as-planned programme to be used to assess delay. It will be necessary to refer to as-built records to establish the effect of the variation on the activity and carry out a sub-net analysis.

6.119 If the event prolongs the duration of an activity by for instance seasonal conditions, then a large discontinuity with actual progress will be highly significant, since the as-planned programme will not allow the activities affected by seasonal conditions to be identified. It will be necessary to refer to as-built records to establish both the activities affected and the delay caused by the conditions.

6.120 In some cases the extent of the disconformity may invalidate the method altogether. In *Great Eastern Hotel Company Ltd v John Laing Construction Ltd* [2005] EWHC 181 (TCC) the expert used an impacted as-planned programme analysis.

6.120.1 Wilcox J rejected the expert's evidence that the late design information either caused or contributed to the critical delay. He observed that the impacted as-planned analysis delay takes no account of the actual events that occurred and gave rise to a hypothetical answer when the timing of design release was compared against the original construction programme. Importantly the analysis took no account of the fact that the design team would have been aware of significant construction delays to the original master programme, and would have been able to prioritise design and construction to fit this – a form of mitigation.

6.120.2 In addition, the analysis compared the timing of the actual design releases against an original programme that was superseded by later versions that showed later dates for the provision of the information required.

6.120.3 The various theories of critical path were considered theoretical constructs identified retrospectively and not identified by either party during the project itself and not supported by the evidence.

Worked Example

6.121 A sub-network of the above critical path network example in Figure 22 is shown below in Figure 23, showing the procurement, design, fabrication and erection of equipment.

Figure 23 – Sub-Network Equipment Installation – Logic with Lags

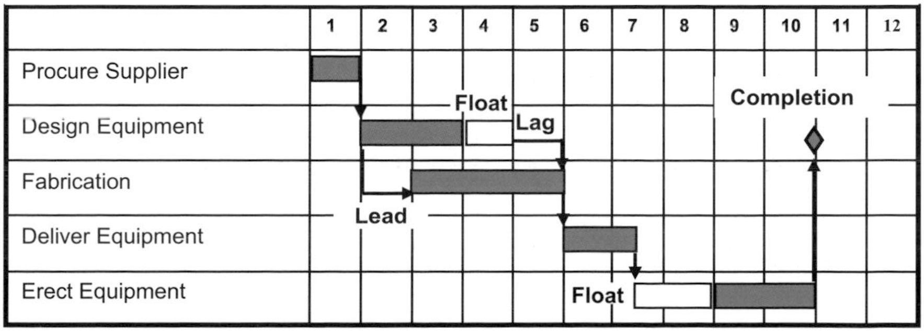

6.122 The logic links between the activities "Design Equipment" and "Fabrication" are shown as *start-to-start* and *finish-to-finish* in order to simplify the presentation.

6.123 In the example, two events affect the commencement of "Procure Supplier" and the completion of "Design Equipment". These are identified as Delay Events 1 and 4. The delay analysis represents the two events as activities with durations equal to the local delay and impacted on the as-planned programme.

6.124 The analysis is shown below in Figure 24 in which Delay Event 1 affected the commencement of "Procure Supplier" – a delayed start - and Delay Event 4 affected the completion of "Design Equipment" – a prolongation.

Figure 24 – Sub-Network Delay Analysis 1

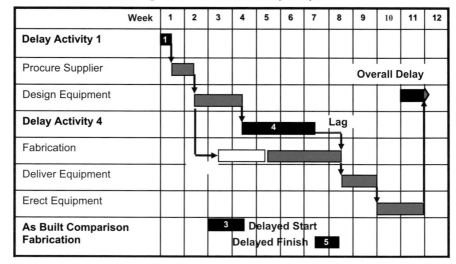

6.125 Delay Activity 4 is shown as a single event prolongation of "Design Equipment". Because of the "Finish-to-Finish" link with "Fabrication", the Delay Event 4 causes a delay to the project as a whole. The analysis takes into account the float and gives a net delay to completion.

6.126 The same example is shown in Figure 15, which shows the comparison of the planned programme to the as-built programme. The comparison is repeated above for "Fabrication" and shows the delayed start and the delayed finish to "Fabrication".

6.127 The comparison shows the lack of correlation of the analysis with actual progress for "Fabrication", which suggests that the analysis of delay is inaccurate.

6.128 An accurate analysis requires the logic links to show the phased design of the activity "Design Equipment". The first part of "Fabrication" starts when the first part of "Design Equipment" has been completed as shown in Figure 25 below. The second part of "Fabrication" starts when both the second part of "Design Equipment" and the first part of "Fabrication" are completed.

Figure 25 – Sub-Network Revised Logic Links – Without Lag Links

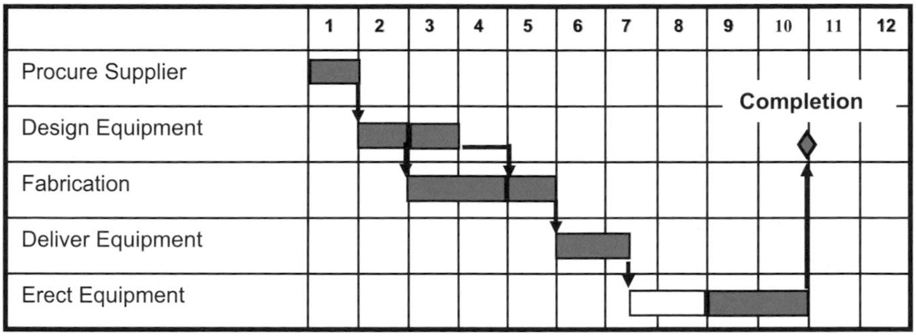

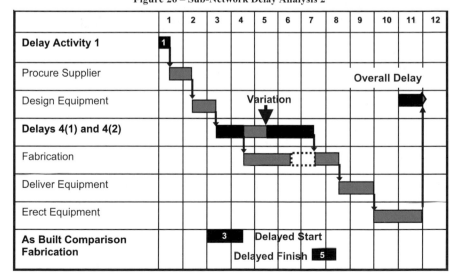

6.129 In this example, the Delay Event 4 is not a single event, but instead separately affects each part of "Design Equipment". One part of Delay Event 4 affects only the first part of "Design Equipment". The second part of Delay Event 4 arises from a variation to the work and only affects the completion of the second part of "Design Equipment". This is shown below in Figure 26.

Figure 26 – Sub-Network Delay Analysis 2

6.130 The revised analysis provides an accurate correlation with the actual delay to the activity "Fabrication", giving some confidence in the accuracy of this part of the delay analysis. This part of the analysis shows that the effect of the Delay Event 4 is to delay "Fabrication" by preventing the commencement of the second part of "Fabrication" and creating a period of standing when "Fabrication" cannot continue. This aspect will be important if the analysis is intended to be used to show the incidence of increased costs.

Judicial Comment on Impacted As-Planned Method

6.131   The impacted as-planned method can be used for both prospective and retrospective analysis, in the administration of projects as well as in the analysis of causation, providing the planned programme correlates with actual progress and is not theoretical. If the critical path of the impacted as-planned programme differs from the critical path for actual progress, then this will cast doubt on the reliability of the method, and in particular as a method for obtaining relief from liquidated damages or the basis of a claim for additional cost.

6.131.1   The method is used where the construction logic has not changed significantly.

6.131.2   The impacted as-planned method assumes that all delay events are equally potent in causing delay and does not deal with concurrency and cannot do so unless the impacted programme properly reflects actual progress.

6.131.3   The method of working will often change or is refined during the course of the project and this should be reflected in the as-planned logic. Frequently the response to an event is a modification to the method and sequence of working. This has an effect on the logic of the planned programme, which must be changed to provide an accurate analysis.

6.131.4   If the actual duration of an activity is different to the as-planned duration, this may be due to a number of causes such as underestimate of the plan, inefficiency of the resources, shortage of resources as well as the consequences of a particular delay event. The cause of the difference must be proven.

6.132   In *John Barker Construction Ltd v London Portman Hotel Ltd* [1996]83BLR31 Mr Recorder Toulson QC considered the entitlement to extension of time under a contract which incorporated the JCT Standard Form of Building Contract with Quantities, 1980 Edition. The method of analysis adopted was an impacted as-planned programme analysis.

6.132.1   Toulson assumed that analysis of the planned programme was an accurate assessment of actual delay. Barker's expert produced charts demonstrating the logical links between the various activities shown in the programme prepared at the time of the acceleration agreement, and further charts seeking to show the effect on those programmes of the subsequent variations.

6.132.2   Toulson broadly accepted the expert's approach although Portman's expert also agreed that the method was in principle a valid way of assessing an extension of time although he had not himself attempted such an exercise in the case. The validity of the method of analysis was not therefore in issue.

6.132.3 Toulson accepted that at the time of the acceleration agreement Barker's planned resources were reasonable for the planned programme. It appears that Toulson considered that it was necessary to be satisfied that the planned programme was realistic as a model for analysis of causation.

6.132.4 Toulson did not fully accept the analysis by Barker's expert and identified that the time reasonably required for some items was concurrent with others and that not every item would have had a direct delaying effect on the completion date. In addition, the expert had allowed a period of delay due to the implementation of instructions, whereas the evidence showed that the Barker had implemented the instructions much earlier. Accordingly, the expert's analysis was required to be modified.

6.132.5 It appears that Toulson required the impacted as-planned programme analysis to be consistent with actual events.

6.133 In *Henry Boot Construction (UK) Limited v Malmaison Hotel (Manchester) Ltd* [1999]70ConLR32 Mr Justice Dyson held that the impacted planned programme approach adopted by Henry Boot was not realistic and did not provide an accurate and logical analysis of delay.

6.134 In *Ascon Contracting Limited v Alfred McAlpine Construction Isle of Man Limited* [1999] (TCC) His Honour Judge Hicks QC recognised that even if a delay has occurred as analysed on the relevant programme at the time, the logic of the programme may change as events unfold and the analysis may no longer be accurate or valid as an analysis of the resulting causes of delay to completion. In particular, intervening events may subsume the previous causes of delay and alter the critical path to completion. Hicks J recognised that if there was such evidence then it would invalidate the causative analysis.

6.135 In *Motherwell Bridge Construction Ltd v Micafil AG* [2002]81ConLR44 Motherwell sought to demonstrate its extension of time to a date which went beyond the date at which liability for liquidated damages would arise, using a theoretical impact as-planned programme analysis based on resources. The additional manhours required to carry out the additional work were used to establish the theoretical extended completion date. Motherwell stated that the analysis showed the date by which Motherwell ought fairly and reasonably to have completed the works after taking into account of the causes of delay which occurred both within and after the time for completion. HH Judge Toulmin QC held Motherwell's approach should be accepted both in relation to extension of time under the contract and in relation to additional costs which Motherwell was entitled to claim for prolongation costs.

The Time-Impact Method

6.136 The "Time Impact" method is also referred to as the "Updated Impact" method or the "Snapshot" technique. The method is based on the as-planned programme but attempts to avoid the criticisms of that method by correlating the planned programme with actual progress.

6.137   The Time Impact method is as follows:

6.137.1 The as-planned programme is updated to take into account actual progress up to the date immediately before the particular event occurred, the "Impact Date". The update includes adjustments of the main dimensions of the as-planned programme, the actual start dates, the actual durations and any refinement or revision of the logic links that have became apparent as the project has progressed. The list of activities may need to be adjusted to accurately describe the method of working. The updated programme then represents a record of progress to the Impact Date and a plan of future progress.

6.137.2 The direct effect of the event is examined by identifying affected activities based on construction knowledge, engineering logic and evidence. Frequently this part of the analysis is carried out as a sub-network with the expansion of as-planned activities into more detailed sub-activities for accurate analysis. The sub-network will usually involve adjustment and expansion of the as-planned logic links.

6.137.3 The results of the examination and/or sub-network analysis are impacted on the updated as-planned programme in the same way as the as-planned impact analysis. The impact analysis will then identify the changes to the planned completion and identify the revised critical path.

6.138   The resulting updated impacted as-planned programme provides an analysis of the consequences of an event on the assumption that future activities will proceed as-planned. In that regard the analysis will be considered reliable only if it correlates with actual progress in the same way as any as-planned analysis. If the analysis is repeated sequentially for each event, then the resulting analysis will provide such correlation.

6.139   The method has the significant benefit that the unfolding of events is replicated in the progressive analysis. By providing a snapshot at each Impact Date the circumstances and background against which actions and decisions are taken can be identified. By providing an explanation of decisions and actions, the method assists in identifying those events that simply arise from the circumstances of previous events and are not truly independent. Similarly, the method assists in identifying those events that are intervening events and reduce previous events to simply part of the circumstances.

6.140   The method itself is not conclusive in identifying the nature of events, since the method requires each event to be analysed sequentially in time without any regard to comparative potency. The central assumption of the method is that the event first in time creates the circumstances for events that follow closely in time. In some cases, it may be more accurate to consider together those events that occur close in time in order to establish whether they are truly independent before impacting the events on programme. This approach is a "Windows" or "Time Slice" Method and described further below.

6.141   The Time Impact method will require many updates of the as-planned programme if there have been numerous events. Considerable historical data is required so that if the updates do not take place during the progress of the project it may be very difficult and expensive to do so retrospectively. If the as-planned programme contains numerous activities and activities, then considerable effort may be required. Often a sufficiently accurate analysis may be obtained by adopting the "Windows" approach described below.

6.4. THE WINDOWS AND TIME-SLICE METHODS

The Time Slice Method

6.142 The Time Slice Method is the progressive analysis of the project over sequential periods that together comprise the total construction period. Each time slice analysis identifies progressive delay and changes in the critical path. The method therefore provides an analytical narrative of the final causes of delay.

6.143 Although it has been stated that the Time Slice Method is not a method of analysis in itself but merely an aspect of conducting the critical path analysis[34], in practice the method usually involves a modified form of time impact analysis of an as-planned programme. The only difference with the time impact analysis described above, is the selection of time periods.

6.143.1 The time periods may be regular intervals such as the periods stated in the contract for reporting or specified periods for the works programme to be updated, when it is called the *windows* method.

6.143.2 The time period may instead be the period between key milestones when it is called the *watershed* method.

6.143.3 The time period may be dictated by the incidence of events, with an analysis of each event or each group of events, when it is called the *snapshot* method or the *time-impact* method which has been described above.

6.144 The analysis will be less reliable in showing the pattern of events the longer the intervals between windows particularly when a number of activities are at or near the critical path[35].

6.145 The Time Slice Method is an important tool in the management of projects. In large or complex construction projects, it is now expected that a critical path network is routinely established and maintained at regular intervals[36].

6.146 The method involves updating the as-planned programme taking into account those activities that had started early or had been delayed and identifying those activities that

---

[34] *Mirant Asia-Pacific Construction (Hong Kong) Limited v Ove Arup and Partners International Limited* [2007]EWHC918(TCC) .

[35] *Mirant Asia-Pacific Construction (Hong Kong) Limited v Ove Arup and Partners International Limited* [2007]EWHC918(TCC) .

[36] *Balfour Beatty Construction Ltd v The Mayor and Burgess of LB Lambeth* [2002] EWHC 597 (TCC).

had started since the previous window. The method allows analyse of changes, identification of problems and delays and allows informed management response. In doing so, it is necessary to examine activities at or close to the critical path. The analysis provides a contemporaneous snapshot.

6.147   The importance of the contemporaneous Time Slice Method in the retrospective analysis of causation is that it provides records and evidence of events and actions.

6.147.1 If the Time Slice Method is adopted during the project, there is more likelihood that accurate information will be readily available.

6.147.2 The longer the interval between windows, the more scope there is for inaccuracy due to poor records.

6.147.3 The method does not substitute the need for accurate and detailed records in order to provide reliable data.

Worked Example

6.148   The interim window network analysis of the example is shown below in Figure 27, incorporating the first two delay events in time, Delay Events 1 and 9.

Figure 27 – Interim Window Network Analysis

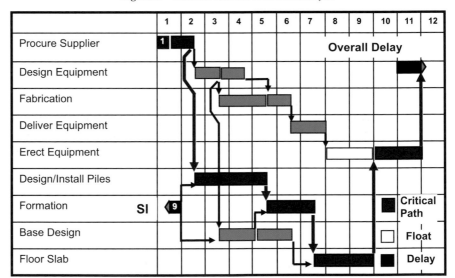

6.149   The worked example shows that the overall delay to completion is greater than Delay 1, which is shown on the critical path. This demonstrates a common feature of complex construction projects in which the restraints and logic links do not become apparent until the project progresses. The worked example above includes additional logic links not shown in previous analysis, between the completion of "Procure Supplier" and the commencement of "Design/Install Piles". The additional link has the effect of predicting a later completion date than previously planned. The revised model demonstrates that the original completion date was not achievable in any event. The later completion date would have been shown in the as-planned programme if the appropriate logic links had been incorporated. That part of the delay to completion is not caused by any event but is due to an underestimate of the time required to complete the project.

6.150   The additional link recognises that until the supplier has been procured and the size and approximate weight and load distribution of the Equipment is known, the design of the piles cannot commence. The cross link is significant because it makes the supply of Site Information non-critical and creates a critical path through procurement and the site construction activities.

6.151   A further cross-link is between the completion of the first part of "Design Equipment" and the start of "Base Design". The link recognises that the interface details with Equipment and particularly items and features to be incorporated or accommodated in the Base are required before the Base Design can be commenced and continue efficiently to completion.

6.152   In complex projects with many activities and logic links, the updating of links during the progress of the project is essential if accurate informed decisions are to be made.

Judicial Comment on Time Slice Method

6.153   In *Balfour Beatty Construction Ltd v The Mayor and Burgess of LB Lambeth* [2002] EWHC 597 (TCC) the adjudicator was presented with various arguments on the appropriate method of analysis for delay and referred to the various authorities at that time.

      6.153.1   His Honour Judge Humphrey Lloyd QC suggested that Balfour Beatty should have produced a time slice analysis. He suggested that any analysis intended to defend against the imposition of liquidated damages must be based on an original programme shown to be valid and reliable, but revised on the occurrence of every event so as to be able to provide a satisfactory and convincing demonstration of cause and effect.

      6.153.2   Lloyd J considered that a valid critical path or critical paths had to be established both initially and at every later material point since he observed that they would almost certainly change. He appears to have considered that it is necessary in order to demonstrate the effect of concurrent or parallel delays or other matters for which the employer will not be responsible, that the constantly changing critical path had to be demonstrated.

6.154   Contemporaneous updates of the original programme are important evidence in the analysis of progress and highly relevant to decisions and actions taken if these matters are in issue. Where the issue is the liability for liquidated damages, it is by no means clear why the constantly changing critical path needs to be tracked by a Time Slice Method of analysis.

6.155   In *Mirant Asia-Pacific Construction (Hong Kong) Limited v Ove Arup and Partners International Limited* [2007]EWHC918(TCC) the issue was the measure of damages for breach of contract.

6.155.1 A significant issue was the identification of decisions in relation to remedial works during the progress of the works which could be considered independent causes or which took the form of negligent advice on which Mirant acted.

6.155.2 If the whole or part of the claim did not arise out of Ove Arup's wrongdoing but from some independent cause then Mirant could not recover damages arising from that cause. Further, the reasonableness of the remedial measures undertaken by Mirant was also in issue. Accordingly, the context in which decisions and actions were taken was highly relevant to the issues in dispute.

6.155.3 Both experts undertook what they called a critical path analysis using the Windows method and it was accepted that Windows analysis was the most accepted method of critical path analysis.

6.5. THE AS-BUILT METHOD

The As-Built Method

6.156 The As-Built Method is an impact delay analysis which is also referred to as the "As-Built But-For" Method and the "Collapsed As-Built" Method. The As-Built Method uses as-built data to identify the start and finish dates for activities. A programme is then constructed by adding the actual construction links to the as-built activities[37].

6.157 The duration of delays are identified and delay activities added to the programme with modification to the actual activity durations and the logic. The programme so constructed is a logic linked programme representing the actual progress of the project. The programme allows the critical path to completion to be identified and therefore those delay activities that are on the critical path.

6.158 The as-built programme is a representation of the progress of the project in which logic has been inferred and the actual events modified by delay events based on deductive analysis. Each step of that process can cause difficulties that affect the reliability of the programme.

6.159 The As-Built Method is expensive to prepare because of the enormous effort required to establish the as-built dates and logic, although some as-built information is usually required whichever method is adopted.

6.160 Different collapse methods are used as a means of deductive analysis by interrogation of the as-built programme. Each is subject to criticism as an analysis of causation in law.

---

[37] The difficulties and reliability of the as-built programme are examined below at Section 5.4 "The As-Built Programme".

The Total Collapse Method

6.161   The *total collapse method* removes all the delay events to establish the "achievable programme" which could have been achieved "but for" the delays. The method establishes the overall delay caused by all the delay events, by calculating the period between the completion date on the achievable programme and the actual date of completion.

6.162   The achievable programme may not correspond to the as-planned programme since it will include all changes in logic and durations that have actually occurred and will be based on actual progress. The accuracy of the analysis not only depends upon the accuracy of the main dimensions of the programme but also the accurate identification of delay events. Proper account must be taken of the contract allocation of risk and there must be an accurate assessment of the delay event.

6.163   The achievable programme can be used to analyse the impact of events in the same way as the Time Impact As-Planned Programme Method. There remain the same difficulties for both methods in the selection of the sequence of events particularly where delay activities are concurrent.

The Default Collapse Method

6.164   The *default collapse method* collapses the as-built programme by removing only those delay activities the responsibility of one of the parties. The resulting programme is then submitted as an analysis of the completion date that would have been achieved "but for" the delays caused by that party.

6.165   The Method suffers from the conceptually difficulties of the "but-for" concept when there are concurrent events[38].

The Identification of the As-Built Dates for Activities

6.166   Frequently, acceptable detailed records are incomplete or not available, so that the reliability of the whole method will be in doubt. Even if records are available they usually do not expressly relate the work to activities required on a programme and may only record that work was being carried out in a particular area. Significant engineering and construction expertise will be required to identify from the available evidence the activities that were being carried out at any time. Frequently only broad assessments can be made with an assumption of continuous working that may not be correct.

6.167   Invariably activities are not completed in an orderly manner, but progressively to allow subsequent activities to commence. Actual activities usually overlap. This frequently occurs on site construction activities when resources are moved to other activities once progress is sufficient to allow a subsequent activity to commence. The work for the incomplete activity may be carried out later to allow commencement of other activities. If there are no subsequent activities which depend upon the

---

[38]   The conceptual difficulties of the "But-For" Concept are examined in Section 2.1 above.

incomplete work it may simply be left as "snagging" at the end of the project. The date when an activity can be considered to be complete may be different for each follow on activity, so that the event identifying completion of the activity must be clearly recorded for any subsequent re-analysis.

The Inference of the Construction Logic

6.168   It is difficult to establish the actual logic of construction from documentary evidence, even if revised method statements and programmes are available. Inevitably, it is necessary to obtain evidence from witnesses of fact and particularly engineers and works managers.

6.169   Considerable engineering judgment is necessary to identify from available evidence the date when an activity was sufficiently completed to logically allow the next dependant activity to commence. Inevitably, the skills required are those of an engineer experienced in construction able to examine witnesses and documents to establish a realistic approximation of events.

The Deduced Delay Activity

6.170   The problem of time disconformities between the assessment of the delay activity and analysis of its effect inherent in the Impacted As-Planned Method does not apply to the As-Built Method. Nonetheless, there remains the requirement to assess the effect of a causative event on the commencement and duration of an activity, in order to determine the properties of the delay activity, the modifications required to other activity durations and the modified logic links.

6.171   In practice, it is necessary to examine the context in which the causative event occurred and establish from that investigation the disturbance caused to progress and the method of working at that time. This is usually carried out using sub-networks which of necessity will involve local comparison of planned to actual progress.

6.172   In addition to factual evidence and sub-network analysis, frequently other analytical evidence is required. This may include engineering reports to identify the effect of a change in design on the method and duration of construction, and productivity analysis to assess the effect of seasonal changes on the duration of activities.

The Reasonableness of the As-Built Programme

6.173   The construction of a project in a particular manner is not evidence of itself that that the progress of the project or the reaction to events was reasonable. The reliability of the as-built programme can be demonstrated by showing that it is a reasonable approximation of events.

6.174   The total collapse method can be used to show that the programme is reasonable if it shows a completion date at or near the required or planned completion date.

6.175 If the achievable programme is resourced to show that it results in a cost approximating to the accepted contract price, this may also suggest that the as-built programme is reasonable. Any large differences need to be explained. For instance if erroneously the reason for the logic adopted in the as-built programme is a shortage of resources or a lack of materials this may show up in the total collapse analysis.

Worked Example

6.176 The As-Built network analysis of the example is shown below in Figure 28, incorporating all four Delay Events 1, 9, 4(1) and 4(2).

Figure 28 – As-Built Network Analysis

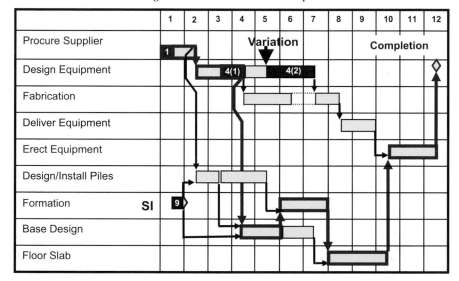

6.177 The example shows the phased design and the cross link of design to construction activities described above.

6.178 The analysis shows that the delay caused by the Variation did not cause delay to completion, because of the crosslink between completion of the first part of "Design Equipment" and start of "Base Design".

6.179 Only the Delay Event 4(1) delaying completion of the first part of "Design Equipment" is on the critical path that includes "Base Design", "Formation" and "Floor Slab".

6.180 The Total Collapse Method for the example is shown below in Figure 29 and shows the Achievable Programme. This shows the delay inherent in the Planned Programme previously described due to the absence of cross links.

Figure 29 – Achievable Programme

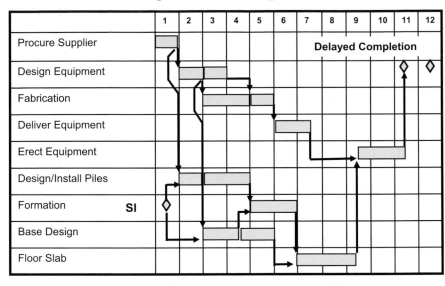

Judicial Comment on the As-Built Method

6.181   In *Henry Boot Construction (UK) Limited v Malmaison Hotel (Manchester) Ltd* [1999]70ConLR32 the thrust of the defence was that the impacted planned programme approach adopted by Henry Boot was not realistic. Mr Justice Dyson agreed and held that under a JCT 80 Form Malmaison was entitled to argue that the Relevant Event was not likely to or did not cause delay because the items were not on the critical path.

6.182   In *Ascon Contracting Limited v Alfred McAlpine Construction Isle of Man Limited* [1999] (TCC)Hickd J recognised that the inference of continuing effect in a causative analysis may be invalidated by events altering the critical path to completion.

6.183   In *The Royal Brompton Hospital NHS Trust v Watkins Gray International* [2000] QBD (TCC) ConLR148 Seymour J emphasised the need to identify those operations which were on the critical path and recognised that it was important to identify the construction logic and observed that the critical path may change

6.184   In *Great Eastern Hotel Company Ltd v John Laing Construction Ltd* [2005] EWHC 181 (TCC) Laing's expert in the main part proceeded retrospectively from an as-built programme to determine the critical path and periods and causes of delay. The method itself was not disapproved, but there was adverse comment on the lack of thoroughness of research and the uncritical acceptance of the favourable accounts put forward by Laing. Despite seeing the photographs and material contained in Eastern expert's two reports received and read by him, totalling undermining the credit and accuracy of a witnesses' account upon which he relied, Laing's expert chose not to revisit his earlier expressed views in accordance with his clear duty to the Court.

INDEX

References are to paragraph numbers

Causation cont.
proximate cause, *see* **Dominant Cause**
value judgment, and, 3.3, 3.43, 3.63 – 3.83, 3.84.5
Collapsed As-Built
see **As-Built**, collapse method
Common Sense
judicial common sense, 1.27 – 1.36
Comparison Method
see **Methods of Analysis**
Compound Causation
apportionment, and, 3.125 – 3.127
Computer Records
evidence, and, 5.62 – 5.64
Concurrency
apportionment, and, 3.72 – 3.83
but-for test, and, 2.18 – 2.23
dominant cause, 1.44 – 1.49
new intervening act, and, 2.47 – 2.51
Conditions of Causation
proof of, 3.31 – 3.32, 3.45 – 3.57
Construction Logic
accuracy of, 6.88 – 6.99
dimension of project, 4.14, 6.71 – 6.74
identifying, 4.25 – 4.27
inference of, 6.168 – 6.169
logical fallacies, 2.11, 4.26 – 4.27
logic links, 6.88 – 6.99
Contemporaneous Records
allocation sheets, 5.65
diaries, 5.61.2
planned programme, 5.41
time slice programmes, 6.147
updated programmes, 6.3, 6.15.4
Contingencies
time risk, 5.31
Continuity
absolute timescale, 5.21
inference of, 4.20 – 4.24
probability of, 4.22 – 4.23
resources, and, 5.33.2
Critical Path
appropriate use of, 1.17, 4.1 – 4.19
causation, and, 4.1 – 4.19
changes in, 4.8, 4.23, 6.131, 6.145 – 6.147, 6.153
construction logic, 4.8, 6.71 – 6.99
definition of, 4.3
float, 6.107 – 6.112
illustration Fig 22, 6.106
method of analysis, see **Methods of Analysis**
near, 4.3, 6.144
network, see **Network Analysis**
Culpable Delay
events occurring during period of,
example 2 - but-for concept, 2.24 – 2.27
example 2 - new intervening act, 2.52 – 2.55
example 2 - principled approach, 3.86 – 3.113

Deduced Delay Activity
sub-networks, and, 6.170 – 6.172
Delay
causation, and,
1.13, 1.43, 1.47 – 1.49, 2.8 – 2.9, 2.39,
3.45 – 3.57, 3.63 – 3.83, 4.1 – 4.19
concurrent, see **Concurrency**
comparison method, 6.1
culpable, see **Culpable Delay**
deduced, 6.170 – 6.172
Delay Analysis
see **Methods of Analysis**
Design
logic links, and, 5.27
Dominant Cause
classification, 1.37 – 1.38
concurrent cause, and, 1.44 – 1.49
identification, 1.40 – 1.49
Duration
accuracy of, 5.31 – 5.34
activity, 5.30 – 5.31
timescale of, 5.21 – 5.23

Effective Cause
see **Dominant Cause**
Evidence
actual progress, 5.59 – 5.67
burden of proof, and, 3.14 – 3.18
delay analysis as, 4.28 – 4.31
documentary, 5.61
expert, 4.29.5
expert use of, 5.59, 5.60.6, 5.58 – 5.59
planned programme as, 5.41
weight of, 5.60 – 5.61
Experts
duty to tribunal, 4.29.5
evidence of delay, and, 4.28 – 4.31, 5.58 – 5.59
Extension of Time
actual delay to completion,
3.45 – 3.57, 3.63 – 3.69, 4.4
fairness and reasonableness of, 4.18
logical analysis of, 4.2, 4.30

Fairness
allocation of risk, and, 1.25, 3.34
apportionment, and, 3.34, 3.39 – 3.83
causation, and, 1.25, 3.34
global claim, and, 6.41 – 6.53
surviving claim, and, 6.50 – 6.52
Fault
apportionment, and, 3.79 – 3.80
Float
critical path method,
4.2 – 4.8, 4.17 – 4.19, 6.103 – 6.112
definition, 6.107